A Nostalgic Look at Your America

SMALL town

Don Padilla

ILLUSTRATIONS BY D.K. SKORO

Preface

The title of this book, with its part capitalization, was chosen to emphasize the SMALLtowns of America, those which by their size had a special distinction.

This distinction was one of closeness, familiarity, and inter-relationships that made a little community seem at times to be one big family.

The towns reflected in these nostalgic vignettes of life in the late 1920s, the 1930s and up to our country's entry into World War II include populations of 350, 400, 750 and 1,500, communities the author has been a part of in Iowa, Minnesota, and Wyoming.

A small town has different meanings to different people. If you move from a major city to a rural area a town of 2,000, 3,000 or 5,000 seems a very small place to live. To someone who grew up in a town of 400 or 750 persons, those same towns of several thousands, usually county seats, were big towns.

If you lived in a town with 3,000 people you very likely did not personally know many of the residents. Not so in a SMALLtown. You knew everybody and everybody knew you.

The stories told in this collection are an attempt to portray what life was like in small towns. Memories and impressions, plus research, are responsible for what appears here. While the author has drawn on his own background as a resource, he believes what is presented to the reader reflects life in all of small-town America.

Acknowledgments

Lots of good friends, many of them SMALLtown folks, read the manuscript for this book for authenticity, offered suggestions, made corrections and additions. The author is indebted to them for their help:

Fred and Arlene Rudi, Jim Moffet, Tom Lee, Tom Henning, Jack and Ruth Moran, David and Nancy Speer, Joe Arndt, Lee and Marie Brown, Gwen Sorlien, Fran and Maxine Gregory, Bill Morehouse, Jerry and Billi Wollan, Jeaner McNaught, Rosie Gregory, Becky Mitchener, Chick McCuen, Bob Elston, Thomas L. (Snuff) Garret, Norman Lorentzsen, Joan Liffring-Zug and John Zug. Doreen Padilla Hyde provided valuable editorial input from the beginning.

Special thanks go to Hon. Elmer L. Andersen, whose encouragement and support made the publication of SMALLtown possible. Tom Swain, Otto Silha, Wheelock Whitney, and David Speer also backed the project and their assistance is greatly appreciated. Jerry Erickson loaned his financial expertise. Illustrator Don Skoro had much good advice as did Allie Skoro. Finally, my everlasting gratitude to Dr. John H. Brown and Dr. Donn G. Mosser, without whose very special help this book could not have been written.

More Books:
SMALLtown may be ordered for $9.95 postpaid, two for $18, from Penfield Press, 215 Brown Street, Iowa City, Iowa 52245.
(1990 prices subject to change).

Contents

Contents *(Continued)*

For

Dagny

Who Was Always There

Hello Central

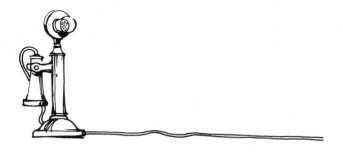

"Hello Central. Say, Edith. Could you ring George at the store for me please?"

"Edith, we've got to talk to Tom. You know, he's down at the state college. He lives in that big dormitory. What's the number? Let's see, they told us to call 297 in that town. Then they said they'll call him to the phone. Thanks, Edith, we'll just hang on here until he gets to the phone."

"Hello, Edith. How've you been? Well, I'm fine, although that arthritis gives me trouble sometimes. Say, Edith, do you know where our church's altar guild is meeting today? I forgot. At Mable Smith's? Thanks. I guess I'd better get ready if I'm going."

"Edith? Hi, this is Marie. I live in the city now, I guess you know that. Say, where's mom and dad today? I should talk to one of them. Oh, mom's at Ladies' Aid and dad at the Farm Bureau meeting. Well, if you hear from them, tell them I'll call Saturday and I'm just fine."

"Edith, we've got a problem. Johnny has fallen out of our apple tree and we're pretty sure he has a broken arm. Do you know where Doc Jones is? He's out at the Phillips farm? Can you get ahold of him and ask him to come to the house? You can? Thanks, Edith. We'll just keep Johnny quiet until he gets here."

"Hi there, Miss Edith. This is Bobby Jones and I just got home and nobody's here and I wonder if you know where my mom and sister are? You do? They said they were going over to my cousin's? Hey, thanks. Guess I'll go over there."

"Hello, Edith. I guess we're going to cancel our plans for this evening. Just can't find a baby-sitter." (Ten minutes later, "Central" calls back. She has checked around, found two girl pals who will be glad to make a quarter each baby-sitting. Our young couple's evening is saved.)

Every week "Central" kept a log on who was "out of town." You called in, let her know where you were going and when you would be back. She knew 500, 600, or even more people, firsthand. Keeping track was important. Since the switchboard usually was in her house, "Central" or one of her family helpers was always on hand (after 9 p.m. emergency calls only). You could ring "Central" at all hours of the night if help was needed. It was her duty and she was dedicated to her job.

She had help. Impossible without it. Everyone in the family spelled "Central." There were times she just had to get away from the "board." The best location for the apparatus was adjacent to the kitchen. That way, "Central" could bake a cake or put together supper and still keep community communications humming.

Sometimes the switchboard was located alongside a front window looking on Main Street. "Central" could give firsthand reports on the weather in town, who was coming into town or just leaving, which way the fire truck was heading. If you were calling for somebody and "Central" saw them crossing the street and heading into the hardware store she reported that to you, connected to the store, and you caught up with your party.

The service was extended. It went like this: "Hello Edith, this is Joe, say I'm heading to the other end of the county on some business and I'm expecting an important call. If it comes through, just leave word at Rucker's store down that way and I'll stop in for the message and phone from there. Thanks Edith."

Out in the country you listened to the rings that were your call, and you listened in on everyone else's conversations. News traveled fast.

That was "Central" in the days when the switchboard was the nerve-center of a small town and the surrounding countryside. And the magic was in the hundreds of lives represented by jacks on the ends of lines, plugged into a forest of holes on the board, criss-crossed in every way, as "Central," headset over ears, performed the daily miracle of keeping the local populace in touch and informed.

In every American small town, no one was more important than "Central."

What's
In a Name

Small towns are friendly, familiar places. Everyone knows everyone and almost everything about everyone.

The familiarity makes life easy, comfortable, without social barriers.

Everyone gets a nickname, sometime. It can happen when you're very young or a circumstance can result in producing a tag at a later date.

If your name is Black and your hair is red, then you become Red Black.

If you are tall and slender, then you become Slim or Skinny. If you are really big you might become Fats. On the other hand you could be Tiny. Don't ask why. It would just happen and made a big guy seem even bigger.

Catfish was given to someone whose feats with a fishing pole approached the legendary.

Behind every name was a story. It gave you standing and you were pegged for life, whether you liked it or not.

Here are some of those names:

Rusty	Hub
Skip	Flash
Scoop	Wheels
Stud	Mumps
Cub	Stretch
Phog (or Fog)	Bud
Sandy	Buddy
Slim	Chip
Goody	Toad
Stub	Swede
Bub	Bus
Skinny	Speed
Goose	Fats
Cope	Ace
Butch	Windy
Blackie	Dude
Whitey	Coffee
Red (as in Red Black)	Peewee
Bull	Deacon
Catfish	Hook
Shorty	Jake
Inch	Bronc
Happy	Squirrel
Lefty	Squeek
Brick	Tin
Tiny (usually over 200 lbs)	Peanut
Dutch	Bull
Hod	Corky
Spike	Lump
Crummy	Spats
Duck	Fipps
Irish	Kraut
Cobb	Pencils

If you didn't have an invented nickname, then your given name was changed to a more familiar version. No one, you see, really ever was called by their formal name.

William became Bill or Billy
Richard was Dick
John became Jack
Peter to Pete
Howard to Howie
Edward became Ed or Eddie
Frederick was better known as Fritz
Robert was Bob
Thomas was always Tom or Tommy
Kenneth became Ken or Kenny
Douglas to Doug
Rodney became Rod
Harold was Hal
Norman was Norm

Many girls or young women had nicknames. Maybe they weren't as prevalent as the men's, but there were lots of them:

Teenie	Stretch
Butch	Speedy (won all the foot races at the school picnic)
Schuppie	Cookie
Ginger	Tex
Tuffy	Charlie
Pete	Scotty (last name Scott)
Puss	Squeak
Jo-Jo	Frankie
Muggs	Johnny
Rusty	Penny
Red	Irish
Pinky	Swede
Slim	Dutch
Norske	Belle
Shadow	Chief

Most had shortened versions of their names, or they had nicknames: Elizabeth became Liz or Beth, Peggy became Peg, Margaret became Maggie, Rosemary became Rosie, Susan became Sue, Christine became Chris, Dagny became Dolly, Marion became Mare, Beatrice became Bea, Doreen became Reenee, Jennifer became Jen, Barbara became Barb, Dorothy became Dot, Charlotte became Char, Maxine became Max or Mack, Phyllis became Phil.

What was important was you had to have a nickname accepted by your peers since nobody every heard anyone calling anyone by their given first names.

There were three exceptions tolerated, but not really accepted by the gang. The three who insisted on proper names were 1. Mom, 2. the Pastor, 3. your teacher.

Oh well, the world couldn't be perfect.

Mulligan Stew For the Town

In the depths of the Depression, events occurred that cost little or nothing, the whole town could participate, and there was lots of fun for all. It took folks' minds off the hard times. That made these events worthwhile.

A town horseshoe pitching contest got a lot of people interested. The competition was keen and a sizable crowd gathered for the finals. The winner was certain to enter the state contest. He would represent the town. Honor and glory at stake here.

In the corn country most communities had a star corn picker. It was the days of the national corn picking contest, followed on radio by hundreds of thousands of rural folks. The local corn picking champ was observed in training as the first corn picking began and then was sent off to the eliminations and, hopefully, the nationals, with the cheers of his hometown friends ringing in his ears.

Baseball was No. 1 in the summer. The town team, made up of high school standouts, old grads, and some with graying hair, battled for the league title in the valley.

Small towns in the West celebrated with an annual rodeo.

A special event was the town's annual Mulligan stew cook-out. It was held each year in a vacant lot next to the blacksmith shop. An ideal spot. For several reasons. It was only a block off Main street. The blacksmith had made the grill and the stand for the grill, and he kept it in his shop from year to year. Also, he was an expert in preparing a stew-cooking fire. He fired up his forge every day. He had the technique.

The blacksmith was in charge of the 50-gallon drum used for cooking the stew. He kept it carefully wrapped and covered in a back corner of the shop until the big day. It was spotless on the inside. Stainless steel. It had been boiled and scrubbed until the inside shined. You didn't want to take any chance of contamination. Too many people would be eating the stew. Sanitary caution was the watchword.

The residents began talking about the annual Mulligan when summer got down to serious heat. The time was coming. A bunch of the boys, and a couple of the women who worked on Main Street, gathered at the cafe and talked over plans. Who would bring certain things? Calls had to be made on the butcher shop and grocery stores for food donations. This was a volunteer effort. No money would be spent to make it happen. That would violate the spirit of the occasion.

A date was set and the effort began. Some folks, especially those with big gardens, offered to bring vegetables. One person was designated to handle obtaining the very best potatoes. Butch at the butcher shop was solicited for beef and pork and some of it could be bones, hopefully with some meat on them (Butch, knowing this was coming up, didn't trim his bones closely for a week ahead of time). The grocery stores tossed in some meat and special ingredients like celery.

The women committee members brought the salt and pepper, Argo starch for thickening, ladles, and miscellaneous other equipment that might be needed. To hold the utensils, a table was brought to the site by a member of the committee.

The crew gathered at 8 a.m. on the dot. The fire was already going and our blacksmith friend had seen to it that the right amount of water was in the barrel from a hose stretched to a well with known high-quality water.

Most folks didn't need to be reminded they were expected to bring their own one-pound coffee can, or similar vessel, and a spoon. It was mentioned, however, by the weekly Chronicle, which had run a story the week before about the big Mulligan stew cook-out coming up. The story told the history of the event. How it had been going on now for more than a decade. Started then by some of the guys at the lumber yard, the grain elevator, and, of course, the blacksmith.

There was a lot of fretting by the committee every year. Worries about the ingredients, the spices, whether this year's stew would live up to the quality of last year's. Everybody said last year's was the best ever. Of course, they had said that in some other years, too. Like the first team in the critical game to decide the championship, the stew committee was charged up to do its best. Make the town proud of this event.

No drinks would be served. If you wanted something to drink, bring your own root beer or pop, or a cup to get that good fresh water from the pump. Alcoholic drinks were forbidden. Nearly half the crowd would be children. The kids flocked to the scene. Spent most of the morning there watching what was going on, listening to the banter of the grown-up folks. It was exciting.

The recipe was practically foolproof. It had been tested over the years and no major changes were tolerated.

Tasting was the highlight of the cooking hours. You watched the tasters to see their reactions. If they had that satisfied smile on their faces, you knew things were coming along nicely. This was going to be a good day.

The signal for the Mulligan eating was the noon whistle. When it blew, the hungry citizens headed for the cooking scene, eating equipment in hand. There were farmers on hand. They had planned some shopping for needed supplies in the morning so they could be on hand for the treat.

It was a colorful crowd, ages 8 to 80. The day was hot, it was the middle of the summer. You sat back to the wall of buildings on either side of the lot to get what shade you could. Some went into the blacksmith shop, especially the ladies. Blacksmith shops were never very clean because of the work done there, but they were cool and that was fine for the ladies. They could stand and eat and chat out of the sun.

The original recipe has been lost in the archives of the past. It has been searched for, but to no avail. The recipe printed here comes from the remembrances of those who were involved. If you want to test it, try a small amount for a handful of people before you launch out on one of the big affairs.

Mulligan Stew For The Town

Use 50-gallon barrel, cleaned so safe for cooking.

Approximately 40 gallons of water.

50 pounds of meat (including bones).

Divided about 60 to 65 percent beef and the rest pork. Cut into dollar-size pieces.

35 pounds of potatoes. Large size. Quartered.

15 pounds of carrots. Cut in half.

15-20 pounds of assorted rutabagas, turnips, parsnips, and beets. Largest proportion should be rutabagas.

A dozen large onions, sweet variety. Cut into chunks.

3 stalks of celery, chopped.

5 pounds of string beans, snapped in two.

Salt, two to three handfuls to taste; pepper, one handful.

Add corn starch at appropriate time.

Bring water to boil. Put in meat and potatoes first. Follow with vegetables at intervals. Let fire cool down to hot coals so stew will simmer for at least three hours.

Serves: The whole town.

Dog

Every small town had its own dog.

The dog didn't belong to anyone in particular.

It belonged to the town. It belonged to everyone. Everyone looked after it. Everyone cared.

Dozens of small boys and girls adopted it for an hour, a morning, or an afternoon, or a day or two.

It was fed by any number of people. But never overfed. Folks watched its condition.

It was friendly. A pal.

It had a sense of owning the town and patrolled familiar haunts.

The names were always the same. Spot, Pal, Brownie, Rex, Dog.

No one knew where it came from, but some said it came from a farm south of town where it was mistreated. It was a pup then. It came and it stayed because it found a home. In the town. The entire town. And with its entire populace. I suppose the dog had a feeling of pride because it served many people, was important to so many individuals from 9 to 90.

It picked out its own sleeping quarters from a large choice of many. The usual was some cozy spot just off Main Street, in an alley, and where it could get inside in bad weather.

In the winter it bunked at the elevator or the lumber yard or a similar place where a convenient opening was left so it could move far enough inside to be out of the wind. More often than not it served sentry duty on the premises during the coldest weather, sleeping by a stove, having been let in by the last to leave for the day.

Someone was always checking it in the off hours. Al, the town marshal and night watchman, looked in on his rounds, had a few words, rubbed it around the ears, scratched its back, maybe gave it a treat.

Mornings, it welcomed all; the first to open up or step outside, then trotting at a good pace, called at a number of Main Street businesses and popular homes. This was a leisurely thing and might take the morning.

Afternoons in the summer were best. Then, it went fishing with the kids or hung out at the playground where someone was bound to play games: chase the ball, bring back a stick, retrieve a piece of wood thrown into the pond. Great fun.

The dog gave the town some of its personality. It tolerated other dogs but really felt superior. More important, you see.

A popular resident, the small town dog.

Whatever Happened To the Shivaree?

In small towns of America, a custom that has pretty much disappeared from our scene is the shivaree.

Shivarees were fun. They were a celebration of somebody's marriage. A salute to the young couple who that day exchanged vows. A sendoff to a successful journey through life together.

The shivaree was as American as the flag, the Fourth of July, and mom's apple pie.

They hardly ever happen anymore and that's a loss for everyone. Another tradition being relegated to the memories of former times.

What was a shivaree? Webster described it as "a noisy mock serenade to a newly married couple." He was dead center. Right on the button.

It certainly was noisy. And it had to be a mock serenade since the din created during a shivaree couldn't be anything else. There was an absence of harmony in the voices raised at the shivaree. And the instrument accompaniment was enough to scare the most courageous of wild beasts into the deepest recesses of the forest.

The shivaree is no longer the small town happening it once was for one simple reason: the newly married couples don't stick around any more; they depart immediately after the ceremony on their honeymoon.

And thus deprive the hometown folks of all that fun.

It wasn't so in the 20s and 30s and up until the Big War.

Honeymoons were something rich folks took. You read about them in the big city newspapers' society pages or in magazines revealing all about celebrities.

This was not altogether true. Young married couples might take a trip later in the year they were married to visit relatives so the bridegroom could show off the bride to his relations and so the bride could show off the bridegroom to her relations. A way of getting a final stamp of approval on the marriage.

The usual timetable of events that resulted in a big shivaree went like this: the lovers were united in matrimony at a morning, early afternoon or evening wedding in the church. This was preceded by a breakfast, lunch or dinner for those participating in the wedding, plus family on hand for the big affair. Whatever the time of day, there was a reception or another festive meal to conclude the day's activities.

Then the newly married couple went home. To the house they had rented, or out to the farm where the big upstairs front bedroom had been prepared for them and was to be their own domain. It would be chores as usual the next morning when it was time to milk cows, slop hogs, feed horses and get things ready for the work day.

Since everybody in town and the countryside knew the newly marrieds, it was only a matter of passing the word where the shivaree group was to meet and a large turnout would assemble— as many as 50 men, women, youths and small children. Everybody was welcome. This was a community event.

All arrived with something in hand; something with which to make noise: a "noisy mock serenade."

If the married couple lived in town, it was a march to the house; if in the country, then cars had to be assembled to haul the shivareers.

The timing was key. Shivarees were always at night and a true shivaree was never at an early hour. Later at night was the correct time, after nine o'clock. A spy was required to bring back the word when the lights in the house were out. In town it was a matter of blocks away. In the country it entailed the cooperation of a friendly neighbor who allowed the cars to park in his farmyard about a mile distant from the newlyweds' abode.

When the signal was given, the army of mock serenaders moved forward, weapons in hand for the assault on the love fortress where the newlyweds were buried in the fruits of love and wedded bliss.

At a signal from the "captain" of the shivaree crew, the shivaree began.

As one shivareer put it, "all hell broke loose."

The cacophony was tremendous.

Town band horns blasted including the usual off-key cornet, adults and kids beat on the bottoms of dishpans and tin pans with sticks and wooden spoons, car horns honked, someone always had a crank-up siren that wailed a deafening sound, a big bass drum boomed, left-over Halloween noisemakers added clacking, everyone yelled and/or whistled— especially the guys who could give out ear-splitting whistles between their teeth. Dogs barked. There were always dogs who came along, they not knowing why but enjoying the party.

It was a celebration.

The shivaree gang was there to help the young couple celebrate their wedding and to get things off to a good start for the new Mr. and Mrs.

Where were the newlyweds and what were they doing?

They were in bed, lights off, but not sleeping. They knew what was coming, or they were pretty sure it was going to happen, 99% sure. They just didn't know when it was going to happen. But if they turned off the lights, that would start things rolling.

They had to wait for the appropriate time until the noisemakers were satisfied that they had made about all the noise it was possible to make, maybe half an hour, and then it was lights on, all over the house.

The newlyweds were called out and it was their duty to show up on the doorstep or the front porch to be cheered by the throng. The couple, attired in robes or a few hastily put-on clothes, had a few words to say— of greetings and welcome.

Then it was everybody into the house for coffee and cookies, punch and cake. Sometimes home brew.

The newlyweds, with the help of family, were prepared with food and drink. Mysteriously, family would show up exactly on time to help serve the "guests."

Shivaree. A special event for the special twosome. Certainly "a noisy mock serenade to a newly married couple," but carried off with sincerity and goodwill by the folks who meant the most to them: family, friends, neighbors, the whole town, and the countryside.

The Heyday
Of a Small Town

Small towns reached their heyday in the 1920s and 30s.

It was before the advent of supermarkets, shopping centers, business concentrations in big towns, paved roads and fast cars, and charge accounts available to strangers.

In their heyday small towns had everything you could want. It was necessary. If it was your town, your community where you identified, then this is where you did your business.

If you needed credit, you got it. Nobody had to ask who you were, ask you for proof of identity. That would be an insult. Folks with jobs got paid once a month. They paid their bills once a month. Farmers paid up when their crops came in and the elevator paid them off. It was convenient. A pleasant way of doing business.

There wasn't any point going to some other town for things you needed to buy. Why, you wouldn't even know those folks in those stores.

You did business with folks who did business with you. Your friends.

It was your town and you were proud of it. Support the old home town. Loyalty was what it was all about.

It made the town strong and kept it in relative prosperity.

Occasionally, folks took the train to the county seat for courthouse business and maybe some services you could only get in a big town. For the ladies it was an excursion and they made a point of looking in on a new dress shop to check on the latest fashions. Then it was a stop at the town's biggest hotel for lunch in the tearoom. Afterwards, it was fun to shop in Woolworth's Five and Ten for a few items. Small towns didn't have a Woolworth's.

The community of a small town—the town itself and surrounding rural farm country—had an uneven radius of five to ten miles. Folks didn't like to travel farther than that unless they had to. It was enough.

If your town had a population of 600 or 700 people, you might have this line-up of stores and businesses up and down Main Street and on the adjacent side streets:

2 banks.

2 grocery stores.

2 drug stores.

2 hardware stores.

Men's clothing and shoe store (also did dry cleaning).

2 or 3 garages. One Chevrolet, one Ford, another could be Hudson, Reo, Graham Paige, Buick or Dodge— or a combination of these. Most garages offered several brands of cars.

2 implement dealers. Almost always operated by the automobile garages.

2 gas stations.

2 cafes.

Harness and shoe repair shop.

Furniture store. Also the local undertaker.

Newspaper and printing shop. Also sold office supplies.

Barber shop.

Railroad station.

Hotel (six to eight rooms, none with baths). One bath down the hall on each floor. Featured Sunday dinner in the dining room. Usually fried chicken.

Tavern. Some towns had two taverns, but not many.

Dentist.

Doctor.

Lawyer.

2 insurance offices (operated out of owner's houses).

Post office.

Popcorn stand. Operated next to bandstand on band nights and Saturday nights.

2 lumber yards.

2 grain elevators.

Blacksmith shop. Horseshoeing a specialty.

Creamery.

Egg buying station. Also a hatchery.

Stockyards.

Movie house. Some small towns only had free street movies.

If you were a town half this size then you might have half as many stores. It all depended. Every town was different. What was there was there because that's what the people needed.

It's all gone now. It disappeared with World War II and the country's post-war economic expansion. Transportation was the main culprit, however. Paved roads and highways and cars that cruised at 50 miles an hour or better sparked the growth of big town shopping centers and they became a mecca for folks from miles around— 20 or 30 miles at least.

Time marches on. The heyday of the small town was over.

Two Kids Meet
On a Summer Day

"Hi."

"Hi."

"Whataya doin?"

"Nothin."

"Whataya doin?"

"Nothin."

"Where ya goin?"

"No place."

"Where you goin?"

"I ain't goin no place."

"Why don't we do somethin?"

"Okay."

"Whataya wanta do?"

"I dunno."

"How bout you?"

"I dunno either."

"You hungry?"

"Little bit, how bout you?"

"Yeah, I could eat somethin."

"Hey, that tree at the Smith's is loaded with ripe apples. Let's go get some."

"Okay."

"Want to do somethin after that?"

"Sure."

"What should we do?"

"I dunno."

"How bout let's walk ditches on the North Road? Maybe we can find enough returns (pop and beer bottles) to get some ice cream."

"Okay."

"One thing, though."

"Yeah, what?"

"Well, if we only get enough bottles so we can buy one ice cream cone, we each take turns lickin. That okay with you?"

"Okay with me."

"You want chocolate, vanilla, or strawberry?"

"I like chocolate best."

"So do I."

"Okay, let's go."

"Yeah, let's go."

Directions

Directions meant something different in a small town. There was North of town, East of town, South of town, and West of town.But points on the compass weren't used inside the town limits which, of course, weren't all that big.

What you did was locate where you wanted to go, where somebody lived, or where something was, by landmarks:

The water tower

Railroad tracks

Churches

Schoolhouse

Stockyards

Goodman's Dairy (where town left off and the country began)

The old factory (they built horse-drawn wagons there in the 1890s and right through World War I and even several years beyond that).

The bottom of the hill

Top of the hill

Lincoln Highway

Either side of Main Street

Cemetery

You could say "just beyond the schoolhouse" or "this side of the schoolhouse" or "the other side of the schoolhouse" or you might say North, South, East or West of same, but not usually. NOT if you'd lived in a small town a long time, or better yet, had grown up there.

Small towns didn't have street signs. You didn't need them.

The streets did have names, but they were in documents buried in the city clerk's office.

Nobody paid any attention to them.

Nobody cared.

They weren't necessary.

You simply identified a street by who lived there, especially who lived on the corners.

It was simple.

It worked.

You didn't need more than that.

Order
Of the Day

Breakfast was in the morning.

Dinner was at noon.

Supper was at night.

Lunch was food served at mid-morning and mid-afternoon to men working in the fields, or extra sandwiches carried in a lunch bucket.

Lunch at noon was something you read about that rich people did in the city. Fancy.

Breakfast time was before everything.

Before work.

Before school.

Before the morning news on the radio.

Before the milking.

Before the stores opened (they all opened by at least 8 a.m.).

Dinner was when the town whistle blew. That whistle meant it was time to sit down and tackle the big meal of the day. At noon. Working people need to be fueled for the rest of the work hours and noon was that time.

Supper was at six o'clock. You knew that because the six o'clock whistle blew and people went home, had supper, usually warmed-up leftovers plus home-canned fruit or pie, and then settled down to listening to the radio: Amos and Andy, Fibber McGee and Molly, Ma Perkins, Jack Benny, George Burns and Gracie Allen, Eddie Cantor, Fred Allen. Earlier, the kids had listened to *Jack Armstrong, the All-American Boy,* and *Jimmy Allen and his Flying Adventures.* Or maybe rocked on the porch, worked in the garden, or visited with the neighbors. The schedule never varied.

It was settling.

Kind of peaceful.

You knew where you were all the time.

It was the order of the day.

Magic of the Rails

Nothing was bigger in a small town than the railroad. Especially if you were on the main line. It connected you to the outside world. It was a symbol of power, of the mightiness of America. America was built on the shoulders of the railroad, the president said. Powerful men like James J. Hill spread the rails across the country and along the way caused towns to be built, farms and timber lands developed, and ranches expanded as beef found a way to Eastern markets.

The railroad meant progress, and many times prosperity. A great labor force was strung coast to coast to keep the railroads running. Section crews, muscles glistening in the summer sun, lifting and carefully setting in place 39-foot rails, tamping in eight-inch ties placed exactly 20 inches apart, kept their seven or eight miles of rails in perfect condition. Railroad men had pride. They were good citizens, faithful lodge members, always ready to help when the town needed help.

There was a hierarchy. The engineers were the kings, the firemen who one day would be engineers were the crown princes, and the conductor was the prime minister. They were looked up to, heroes to small-town boys. Every boy worth his salt wanted to be an engineer some day. To be behind the controls of a huge engine powered by boilers fueled by blazing coal, barreling through the countryside, whistling their message into the wind "caution, stop at crossing, beware of train coming, clear the way." A huge engine towing passenger and mail cars or a long line of freight cars with caboose bringing up the rear.

Forget college or the family business. Go to work for the railroad. Become an engineer one day. Heady stuff. It took great argument by parents to turn young heads to the paths of higher education, other endeavors. Who would want to be a bank president when you could be the engineer of the "Limited"? Why, it was better than being All-American. All-American didn't last long. You could be an engineer for half a century. Some did that. They were the ones who "grew up on the tracks," went to work for the "road" when they were still in their teens. Many of the great railroaders came from railroad families. They grew up on the tracks living in "railroad houses." They would have a large 18-carat gold watch some day. The mark of a railroad man. His timepiece was his most important instrument. It would be a 21-jewel Elgin, size 16, non-magnetic with a hair spring. Standard for all top railroaders. A standard of accuracy that was very rigid—

right to the second. It had to be. "Old 45" had pride. It kept its schedules. Hundreds of towns and thousands of their residents depended on the train being on time.

The railroad was romance. People going to fascinating and far places. Places most folks had never seen, only read about. You looked at the folks in the windows of the passenger cars as the train stopped briefly at the station and you wondered where they were headed, what interesting journey they were on to some distant destination where there would be something exciting awaiting them.

The people who made up the train crew— engineers, firemen, conductors, brakemen, porters— had an air about them, a style. They were men of the world. Part of the romance. They were always on the move. They went places and saw things you could only imagine when you lived in a small town. But some day it would be different. You would be on that crew. Or a passenger going places, doing things. Seeing America.

Once in awhile a family in town would take the train to Glacier Park and stay at the big hotel. They would send postcards back showing the hotel, the beautiful mountain lake, the Indians in full regalia who danced ceremonial dances for the hotel guests. The weekly Chronicle did an article about these folks and their trip. Postcards were passed around town. When the family came home they were besieged with questions about the trip. There was lots of storytelling.

The train brought goods to town, hauled away the grain and livestock from the farms. It also brought the drummers— salesmen with their trunks of sample goods to show local merchants. They stayed at the hotel near the railroad station. They seemed all-wise. They were travelers in America. They saw much, knew much. You knew that by just looking at them. Their comings and goings were noted in the weekly Chronicle. The salesmen made sure they stopped at the Chronicle to say hello to the editor. Publicity helped sell cream separators, dresses, hardware, overalls, socks and shoes.

The train also brought hobos. Some towns tolerated hobos, some didn't. Hobos knew what to expect, good or bad, by the signs left by their comrades of the rails.

The station was transportation headquarters and the station agent was a very important man in town. He managed all things local for the road: sold the passenger tickets, handled the freight, saw that the crossing guard, often himself, was always on the spot when a train was coming through. He was an information center for travel and for transport of goods, kept the town abreast of railroad doings and changes in train schedules. He was the main contact for the shippers. He performed a myriad of tasks while extending goodwill for the railroad, including allowing young boys and girls to watch fascinated as he tapped his important message out across the telegraph lines: railroad messages, shipping orders, telegrams from townfolk. He was the emergency link to the outside world, often relaying the message of birth or death or of other critical situations. "Urgently need money." "Come home at once, family member critically ill, let us know which train, we will meet you at the station."

The railroads were years ahead of highways, most of which were yet to be built. The train was the best way to travel. Social columns, the personals in the weekly newspaper, reported all goings and comings on the train. A trip to the county seat seven miles away was a special occasion: "Mrs. Nel Smith and daughter Jo Ann took the 10 o'clock Thursday morning to Center City where they shopped, stopped at the courthouse to see Sheriff Tom Flannagan, an old friend of the family, and visited the home of Mrs. Smith's cousin, Mrs. Bill Werner. After a tasty luncheon, the Smiths returned home in the afternoon on the 3 o'clock."

The town hummed with railroad activity. On the main line it could be eight or ten passenger trains or more and two or three times that many freights. It depended on the line and the season. The railroad was the nerve center of transport and communication. There was mystery and magic in trains and railroading. The click-clacking of telegraph keys, the signal lights, the steam from mighty engines, the strings of freight cars you counted as they went by, the happy passengers off on a trip sealed inside a magic carpet.

It lasted a long time, this magic. It's gone today, but not forgotten. The railroad made small towns important, helped them to prosperity, linked them to the country and the world.

No one who was ever part of this will ever forget his first train ride, usually just a few miles. Later, there was a trip to the state capital or the State Fair and once in a young lifetime a trip out west. Dinner in the diner. Climb into the pullman bed. Look out the windows as you sped through the night. Glimpses of small towns, big towns, railroad yards.

Memories. The railroad played a key role in American life and your life, too.

Eatin' Your Way Through Town

Kids in small towns were the best-fed kids in the U.S.

Not only did they fare very well at home with three square meals a day under the watchful eye of mom, who demanded a clean plate after such admonitions as "you're getting these vegetables because they're good for you, now eat them."

Boys, in particular, also fared well elsewhere when it came to being fed.

Especially during the growing and ripening seasons and especially during summer vacations from school when there was plenty of time to leisurely eat your way through town during a busy day of having fun, enjoying the good life in those years until you reached your teens. When you reached your teens, boyhood was over and all kinds of work situations suddenly entered your life signaling the end of the carefree days when you were just kids.

Small towns had traditional features. One of them was that everybody had a garden. It was rare to find a household that didn't harvest from their back yard. Folks were proud of their ability to grow things. Vegetables flourished under their green thumbs. Sweet corn was always tender and delicious; the potatoes were the best.

There were fruit trees everywhere. Folks enjoyed fresh fruit, made jar upon jar of jams and jellies, and put up quart jars of peaches, plums, apples, pears, and cherries. The sounds of canning were heard out of many a kitchen window. The apples were carefully boxed and put down in the cellar to keep for winter consumption.

It was a perfect setup for young pals who had hearty appetites. Young pals who would be traveling around town during the day, visiting each other's houses, playing ball in the schoolyard, or checking on pet rabbits and pigeons and assorted other animals.

Starting at snack time, about mid-morning, you could stop at a friendly garden to pull a couple of carrots, wash them under a handy pump, and eat away. The same went for tasty young green onions. Also for rhubarb. When the tomatoes ripened there was nothing more tasty than a red ripe tomato fresh from the garden.

Later in the season a fresh-dug potato could be peeled with a jackknife, washed under the pump and munched on. Somehow, eaten this way, they tasted just as good as the cooked item.

As the day wore on one could enjoy a hatful of cherries picked from a convenient tree. Then there were juicy plums, tart pears and loads of apples of a dozen kinds— all good.

Why, in one day's rambling a boy could feast on a number of nature's finest products. A noon meal hardly seemed necessary, although almost always somebody's mom offered a sandwich, milk, and a piece of cake or a cookie. This necessitated calling home to say you wouldn't be there for dinner (dinner was always at noon), but would be home in good time for supper.

Both mornings and afternoons were good for eating your way through town. It just depended on your appetite. There was plenty to be had. No problems with the supply. If you weren't eating off a friend's trees or gardens you could just ask anyone at home anyplace if "they minded if you had a tomato from their garden or an apple from their tree." The answer was always, "go ahead, but be sure you don't step on the beans, or don't shake the tree, just pick what you want."

It was great. A boy's smorgasbord. A food utopia.

Funny though, when a guy sat down to supper, there were times when you weren't hungry and mom would want to know "why aren't you eating your supper?"

Well, the only reply you could make was, "Gee, mom, I guess I'm just not hungry tonight. It must be the weather."

Things to Hunt That Were Pretty Good Eating

Hunting was a way of life in small towns. You grew up learning to shoot a BB gun, then a single-shot 22 rifle, and finally, a shotgun. There were plenty of teachers. Older brothers, dads, uncles, friends of the family were always ready to teach you about firearms, gun safety, the techniques of successful hunting.

Being the proud owner of a single-shot 22 was a mark of having achieved early manhood. Rifle resting in your arm, muzzle pointed down, you headed for the woods, fields, and marshes. Sometimes alone, sometimes with a buddy. You had status. You would be a provider for the family kitchen. Wild game on the table when your folks were struggling to find money to pay for needed groceries was appreciated by all. You couldn't get enough of it. Keep the game coming in all fall and winter. Man had been a hunter since earliest civilizations. You were living up to the heritage.

Money for shells was a problem. Whenever you could earn a few nickels and dimes running errands, helping someone move, or finding and selling reusable bottles, you bought shells. The friendly firearms dealer didn't make you buy a box of shells at a time. You couldn't afford that. He understood. He sold you three, four, five or ten shells if that's all the money you had.

You prided yourself on being a good shot. You worked at it. Ammunition was too expensive to miss. And many times you were in the field hunting with only a few shells. Every one had to count.

From area to area, the game varied. But the range was great.

Rabbit

Squirrel

Pigeon

Pheasant

Quail

Duck

Goose

Grouse

Prairie Chicken

Possum

Deer

Raccoon

Today, pheasant, quail and duck are gourmet fare, but there was a time when they were just table meat.

There were other kinds of hunting. You hunted turtles.

Not with a gun, with a stout stick, and then grabbed them with your hands. Getting good, fat turtles meant crawling along creek banks, feeling for the shell that told you the game had been found. You hunted fox for the bounty and the skins.

Wild game spiced up the menu. A diversion from beef, pork and chicken. Turtle made great stew. Maybe the best stew ever. But it took a good cook to get the stew just right. Women who were good turtle cooks had reputations far and wide. Pigeons were best served in a pigeon pie with thick, rich crust. Possum had fans and detractors. Some liked it, some didn't. Raccoon was popular with some and it was rich meat.

The cottontail rabbit was the most popular game. Fried rabbit, biscuits and gravy was a favorite dish. Jack rabbits were hunted and wound up on the table but they could not compare with the cottontail.

Wild game menus were flavored with mushrooms you hunted for in the woods and stored in the root cellar, and wild berries put up in jars.

If you were lucky enough to get a deer you had a good start on the winter meat supply. Venison steaks, chops, hamburger, and sausage were kept where below freezing temperatures preserved the meat. The "freezer" often was a corner of a shed or garage. If you got a prolonged warm spell, the snow melted and the grass acted like it wanted to grow again, you ate a lot of venison, as much as three times a day, so it wouldn't spoil. Some folks tried canning deer meat, but were not very successful.

Times were different then. Hunting was exciting and a challenge. You didn't want to come home empty-handed. But you weren't after trophies or out to see whether you could bag your limit. You took home what you could eat. That's when the hunting ended for the day.

It had been the same for thousands of years. You were just carrying on the tradition.

The Great
Watermelon Caper

Every year, in the late summer, an annual rite took place in many a small community. A tradition observed faithfully. Carried on from generation to generation.

The great watermelon caper.

You were in high school, probably an athlete, in good shape and able to run with the wind. This was important. There were times when you needed to run well ahead of flying buckshot. Whether it was really aimed at your departing backside isn't important. The loud blast of a 12-gauge in the hands of an irritated watermelon grower, whether aimed to hit or to scare, was enough to make an Olympic sprinter out of anyone.

During the warm mid-summer months there was much scouting to determine the best patches and a good deal of conjecture as to the best methods to raid the patch for the succulent fruit. One didn't want to launch an expedition until he was certain the melons were at peak ripeness.

Intelligence gathering solved this. You watched to see when a grower brought a first delivery of watermelons to the grocer. You stopped by the store, "knuckled" a few promising looking ones to determine by the sound if ripeness was at peak. You could even talk the grocer, or one of his help who could be a friend working a summer help shift, into plugging the melon. Taste test was sure fire.

The melons were ready. The time had come. Action.

There were daylight raids. There were night-time raids. There was deception and subterfuge. Rules were observed. You never raided a melon patch during Sunday church services. Unfair. There was competition involved here and fairness meant something. Even though the odds were in your favor. The farmer or melon patch operator was one person— maybe with help from a hired man. You were six to a dozen in your squad. Enough to create diversion, initiate flanking movements. Deception was part of the strategy.

The farmer knew you were coming. He just didn't know when. Advantage your side. This was competition. To the winner went the spoils. Delicious juicy watermelons. Fruit of the gods on a warm, late summer night.

Swiping watermelons was never thought of as stealing. The gang could afford to buy a couple of watermelons if they were just hungry for watermelon. No, that wasn't it. It was the tradition and it was fun. The county sheriff, the town marshal, the mayor, all looked the other way when this "rite of late summer" occurred. Not that officialdom didn't threaten, warn, and once in awhile provide such punishment as your compensating the farmer if you were caught and hauled before the "bench."

The town observed what was going on. "Heard the boys were out for watermelons last night. Old Jud fired a few blasts at whoever was in his patch but didn't wing anybody. Guess they got away with a back seat full of melons. Son of a gun if those boys ain't something."

The daylight raid was the most daring. The best ploy involved two cars. In one car were two of the gang. They would make the frontal approach. The other car held the remainder of the bunch. They would come in from the backside after a roundabout trip that kept them out of sight and allowed them to park their car where it couldn't be seen.

Now the diversion. The deception. The sting.

The 2-man squad drove into the farmer's yard, announced they wanted to buy a watermelon and proceeded to keep the farmer occupied until his patience was tested as they checked melon after melon. Rap, rap, rap. "How about plugging this one?" Or, "could we move some of these to get at that big one down there?"

Meantime, the four or five-man squad was quietly creeping into the patch some quarter of a mile away and carefully selecting and carrying away one perfect melon each plus two for the guys keeping the grower occupied. It worked every time. The farmer got maybe 15 or 20 cents for a nice big watermelon but gave up seven or eight of his best in exchange.

The tried-and-true method of obtaining watermelons, though, was at night, usually just as the lights went off in the house of the grower. He was in bed, perhaps asleep. But was he? Many the time the boys thought they had it made only to discover the farmer was up to one of his old tricks. He had hidden himself in the patch and his wife had turned off the lights at the regular going-to-bed time to complete his deception.

This made for a "hairy" situation. When the farmer rose out of the melon patch, shotgun elevated and looking like a field artillery piece, the hair stood straight out on one's neck. Drop the melons and run. Run like crazy. Dodge every which way. Zig Zag. Broken field running at its peak. Pray don't trip. Blasts from the gun. Shot raining around you. Front and back. Close. Boy, was that close.

It wasn't always lead shot. Sometimes rock salt. One grower dried watermelon seeds and loaded his shells with them. True justice, he figured, if someone was rear-ended with watermelon seeds.

Mostly, though the night forays were successful. The farmer or grower had to get his sleep. He couldn't hang around the patch every night. Anyway, he had planted a few extra rows of melons figuring the boys would get away with some. Play the percentages.

There was nothing to compare with a watermelon raid. What else could make the blood surge, the adrenalin race like a foray into the patch? The flush of success kept one tingling for hours. Hard to get to sleep after a night like this. Being full of tasty watermelon was very satisfying.

Not always, though. In one case the farmer caught the boys red-handed. They couldn't get away. The menacing double-barrel was in his hands. His punishment? He made them sit and eat all— all, that is— of the watermelons they were trying to get away with. Then he made each one of them carry over another large watermelon from the pile and he made them eat that. He made them eat melon until with pleading eyes they begged until he finally let them go with the final comment, "Well, I hope you guys have had enough watermelon for this summer. I don't want to see you back this way again."

They didn't return. That was enough. Watermelon up to their ears. No one had ever eaten that much water-melon in one sitting. The watermelon raids were over.

That is, until next year.

The Town Drunk

Why we'll never know, but for some reason small towns always had a Town Drunk. If the title is capitalized that's on purpose because it was deserving. He was something special. Not necessarily to be admired. And certainly not to be looked down upon.

It was just a plain fact. There was one person in town who occupied this post of dubious honor and did it with gusto.

He could be counted on. On all special days and special occasions: Fourth of July, Decoration Day, Labor Day, the town's anniversary, the annual Booster Club carnival days, the Bullhead fry to raise money for the volunteer fire department, the parade down Main Street when the football team won the River Valley Conference title, New Year's of course, and all national celebrations observed by the American public.

Without question, the biggest occasion of all was the day prohibition ended in 1933. It was the Town Drunk's very special day of a lifetime. For the first time it would be okay just to walk up to the bar and order a drink. No more lurking in alleys to have a pint of corn whiskey passed and take a few slugs, or a quiet three taps on the right back door to have a bottle quickly handed out and money handed in. Now, he was a citizen, a star-spangled American citizen, enjoying his rights of buying whiskey legitimately.

It made a fella feel good, made him feel whole.

This was not an occasion where this special citizen celebrated the day. No sir. It was bigger than that. This one went three days and there was speculation on Main Street it might go a week. Bets were made.

But sobering up on the fourth day ended this event. It was enough. There was just so much cheering one could do over something like this. And three days of saluting the President, members of the congress, governors, mayors, the town council and every other kind of elected public servant whose influence might have had something to do with the change in the law with "bottoms up and pour another one" was right at the limit of endurance.

Plus that it was time to go back to work. Economics dictated it. The larder was bare and some solid food would be needed in the days ahead to get strength back. After all, there would be another community celebration coming up soon and there was his obligation to consider.

The Town Drunk was a kind person. Smiled a lot. Joked, too. He was well liked. Never offended anyone. Didn't get in anyone's way. Was always ready to lend a helping hand.

It doesn't mean he wasn't frowned on. He certainly was by the leading church women of the town, and several of the elders were wont to cast a critical eye on our friend.

That was the key to his success. He was a friend. Friendly. Everybody's friend. Who else in town could claim the same distinction? It was his. Fact of the matter is between the work he did to keep body and soul together and fulfilling his liquid destiny there was not time or energy left to do anything else but be friendly.

He liked being friendly and he liked being liked.

There was a puzzling aspect to the Town Drunk. For some reason unexplained he usually was a painter and hanger of wallpaper.

One sage in town claimed it was the ingredients in the paint and the aroma coming out of a gallon can of the stuff that turned a man to drink. This was never substantiated although a member of the council did ask a friend at the state college to check and see if there was anything to this idea. The reply was "no and it isn't worth spending any of the college's time and money to investigate such a crazy theory."

The role of the Town Drunk wasn't one to be envied. It simply was there, a fact of life and the town was certain when the role was given up because he had been "called to the roll up yonder" there would be someone to succeed him. Several candidates had been noticed over a period of time with one person appearing to be in the lead. Sure enough, he was a painter and occasionally hung wallpaper.

Moms did not shoo the kids away from our character. They held him up as one not to be emulated and "what happens to boys when they don't mind their mothers and go to Sunday School without complaining."

The kids were always on the lookout for the Town Drunk during a big celebration and would take their friends to observe him when he was sleeping it off on a summer night in a grassy spot in a back alley.

Another question was "How was this honor achieved, how did one become the Town Drunk?" Obviously, a well cultivated taste for the "devil's brew" was one part of it.

Then there was a dedication to the task. Pride in what one did. Not to mention the enjoyment of a job well done.

Even the most critical had to say "the man sure went at it in a big way. Never saw anything like it. Why, if I ever drank like that they'd soon have me six feet under."

Stamina. It takes stamina to be a champion. A noble effort to be the best at whatever your game. Winners are winners. No matter what the challenge is or the competition.

One couldn't help but admire a leader in his field.

Even if it meant being the Town Drunk.

When Outhouses Were Still in Style

Outhouses did not go out of fashion or usage in small towns until the eve of World War II; later in some far inland villages.

It depended on when your town installed a municipal sewer system and when folks could afford to hook up. The folks on the outskirts of town, and many of those houses were on farms, saw no immediate need for a change— not when money could go for a new plow or repairs to the tractor.

What folks had been doing, what they had been accustomed to for years and years, wasn't something that needed urgent attention. Besides, the hooking up of the new sewer system cost money and that was just the half of it. Installing a bathroom in the house (if you were going to put in a toilet you also had to put in a cast iron tub) meant plumbing and carpentry. And you had to find a place to put the darned things.

A common occurrence in the early days of indoor bathrooms was the freezing of pipes; insulation wasn't very sophisticated and a common sight on a frigid winter day was a neighbor thawing out pipes with a blowtorch. For most folks it was a big change in the lifestyle.

The "it served us well for many a year" outhouse with quarter moons cut in the sides or the door for ventilation, was down the path, close to the alley.

The town wise man said it was "too far in the winter" (a cold, snowy walk) and "too close in the summer" (the breeze carried the aroma in through open windows).

It was not lighted.

It was "air-conditioned": hot in summer, cold in winter.

You could say it was primitive. You either traversed the path by the light of the moon or carried a kerosene lantern or flashlight for the night run.

When it was below zero, the old outhouse was a situation to test anyone. Long underwear wasn't enough. If it got too blamed bad, there was always the chamber pot. A practical answer, particularly where small children were involved. In the summer you worried about bees and wasps. Unwelcome guests in the confines of an outhouse.

It really wasn't possible to do much decorating. Some folks tried to dress up the place with leftover wallpaper. Some tried painting flowers or designs on the inside walls if they were artistic.

The Sears and Roebuck and Montgomery Ward catalogues were the standard toilet paper in those times. People didn't start buying toilet paper until the advent of inside facilities. Then the stores started stocking the stuff (there hadn't been any call for it before). The catalogues served the populace well. The bonus was the reading.

You could study up on what you might be needing in goods or supplies, you could dream a little when you looked at fancy things that might be a little out of financial reach, and you could learn how things worked by just reading the descriptions and instructions.

Boys and young men learned from the catalogue the secrets of what was worn under dresses. Education.

The yellow, thin index pages were the best. They were the softest. They came from the previous year's catalogues. The current catalogues, "Bibles of buying", were kept inside the house on a handy shelf. Last year's catalogues were in the outhouse. So you were always a year behind.

Training the kids to use the outhouse was not an easy task. It took prodding, encouragement, cajoling, threats, intimidation. Places like schools were among the first to have indoor plumbing. Lots of kids "held on" or hurried to school to visit the "Boys" or "Girls" before the bell rang for the first class. So warm and cozy— sure beat dashing out to a cold outhouse on a frosty morn.

Some folks were sensitive about their outhouse. They saw it as a necessity, but not something to admire or be proud of. They simply had to put up with it. There were folks who tried to disguise it with trellises and flowers, or a grape arbor and lots of hollyhocks. Hollyhocks flourished along the outside of outhouses. They've never been known to do as well anywhere else.

Halloween was a tough time for outhouses.

The sport of tipping over outhouses on this night was a major event of the year in a small town.

The "gang" gathered at the darkest hour and the boys proceeded (after a strategy session) to run from one end of town to the other, tipping over every outhouse in their path.

The town marshal, and whoever he could deputize for the night, would be trying to catch the gang; round up the culprits and haul them before the mayor or justice of the peace for due punishment. Seldom was the gang caught. If the gang, or part of it, was caught, then there was a "dressing down," the threat of incarceration overnight (the jail was far too small to hold the gang) and, finally, agreement the sentence would be lifted if the gang assembled at 8 a.m. the next morning and went around town and righted the structures they had so gleefully tipped over the night before.

But the town marshal and his troops almost never caught the gang. The gang, most of them high school athletes, were just too fast, and the law didn't know from which direction the raid would start, or where it would end up. The gang would vanish into the night to a dozen hideouts where the culprits could regale each other with tales and excitement over the evening's adventure.

There was always the element of danger. More than one sly, crafty outhouse owner, bent on revenge since the year before, would move the little building just a few feet back, leaving the opening in the ground, which he carefully covered with twigs and grass. Rushing up for the great tipping effort, more than a few of our young friends would wind up victims in the "pit." Clotheslines, especially the wire ones, had to be watched for. They were hard to see on a dark night. If you charged into one, you were certain to be bruised and knocked to the ground, maybe your breath knocked out. A red mark on the neck the morning after Halloween was a sure sign of mischief.

The beginnings of World War II coincided with the last days of the outhouse. The smallest towns were the last bastions of this American institution since, like everything else, the big towns and cities seemed to get the modern conveniences first.

Progress came slowly to small towns. There was no hurry. That's the way folks felt.

It sure was a comfort to have a nice, warm indoor bathroom. But it was sort of sad to see the old outhouse go. It held so many memories. So many hours of good reading, and contemplating, and planning and plotting. It was where you smoked your first cigarette (a hand-rolled Bull Durham), dropping the butt down in the depths so there would be no trace.

It was where you secretly read your first risque magazine or book.

It was where you had a confidential talk with a pal.

Gone now, but not forgotten. The outhouse. A part of history.

Flour Sack
Fashions

During the 1920s, the 30s and through World War II the flour sack dressed much of America.

It worked two ways. Housewives, mothers and working women needed cloth at little or no expense for making dresses, blouses, nightgowns, aprons, and other female attire for all ages. Children needed playsuits, rompers, little shirts and blouses, and something to sleep in. Shirts, night shirts, shorts and pajamas were needed for men and boys.

The milling companies needed sales promotion to move their vast quantities of product in a highly competitive industry; printed flour sacks were the answer. Plus that they could always sell excess printed bags and thus recover some of their expense.

The appeal was tremendous. The demand was there. These were the decades of thrifty living, the stock market crash, the Depression, WPA, the drouth that scorched much of the Midwest and the Southwest.

There was money to buy flour. You had to have bread. Staple of the diet. The flour millers offered up flour in dozens of romantic, exotic and historic names: American Beauty, Belle of Waco, Ben-Hur, Betsy Ross, Can Do, Cinderella, Daniel Webster, Dixie Delight, Elk Horn Best, Fast Flyer, Four Aces, High Life, Iron Duke, Pollyanna, Parisian, Radiance Rose, Robin Hood, Sunbonnet Sue, Top Hat and White Deer, to name a few. Make it interesting and fun to buy flour. And the bonus was the sack itself, ready to make into a new garment.

For many families there was little money left for luxuries like yard goods. Yard goods were bought for special apparel for special occasions. Otherwise, the good old flour sacks would do. An accumulation of fancy printed flour sacks led to intensive sessions at the sewing machine with the entire family getting something new to wear.

Milling companies outdid themselves in coming up with attractive designs for their Gold Medal, Occident, Big Jo or Pillsbury's Best bags. They produced patterns, sewing instructions and idea packages, including pamphlets showing all the handsome things you could do with their "good quality" cotton cloth colorfully imprinted.

Although both city folks and town folks made the most of this bonanza, the flour-sack look was most noticeable in the small towns and their rural countrysides. The cities had different levels of affluence. The upper structures of this society kept legions of tailors and dressmakers and manufacturers of yard goods busy. In the cities it was the working folks in the factories and industrial lofts who made things out of flour sacks to keep the family neatly dressed.

In a small town a flour-sack dress was not that appealing to a girl turning young woman in high school. Many times it was all she had to wear. She was self-conscious about it. She knew that everyone knew her dress was made out of flour sacks. You could tell by the style. By the look.

Nothing to do about it, though. Times weren't easy. There wasn't enough money for everything you wanted. Take things the way they are and be grateful. Better times would be coming.

Twenty-five years later this same young lady, now a woman with a successful career of her own, a husband with a good business, and achieving children, would be back in town for her class reunion wearing beautiful clothes with New York fashion house labels. She had made it all the way. Everyone was happy to see the transition, never forgetting her days in flour-sack dresses. But it would always be with her and she never denied her good fortune in having a mother who labored into the night at her sewing machine to keep her dressed as best she could. She was thankful for that. But life was more than flour-sack dresses. You wanted the finer things in life. When hard work produced them the satisfaction was profound.

Most folks were just happy to have something clean and bright to wear. Men looked silly at times with summer shirts that were a little too colorful because of patterns that were better suited to something a lady might wear. So what. A new shirt felt good and a little color was good for the spirits. The kids romped and played in whatever you put on them. The boys, though, had to have overalls. Just like dad's. Important to start looking and acting like a man early in life.

When the flour sack fashion craze hit, the Household Science Institute said it would not be surprising if the fad swept the country. The Institute was right. The fad swept the country and millions of flour sacks wound up on the backs of America.

It wasn't long before housewives were able to think of dozens of uses to which empty flour bags could be put. The 48-pound and 98-pound bags were most readily adapted to clothing. If you were anxious to get at the sewing machine and you lacked a few bags the bakeries always had extra bags to sell at 10¢ each. This worked better in the cities or the big towns. Most small towns didn't have bakeries. You did all the baking at home yourself. Send a dollar plus postage to a friend in the city and get ten bags.

The milling companies hired home economics experts and designers to coax American women into baking more and thereby using more flour and having more sacks by enticing promotions. Needlework designs were printed on 24-pound and 98-pound sacks. Five-pound sacks were imprinted for doilies and handkerchiefs.

Companies were ingenious. One described its patented apron bag as a "bag, standard size and quality, regular flour bag cloth, which is so fabricated that it offers a complete apron ready to wear when emptied, turned, ripped and washed."

Even President Calvin Coolidge, "Silent Cal," got into the act. The ladies of the Millard Ave. Presbyterian Church in Chicago got together to make a "smartly tailored" pair of pajamas a gift to the president to show their "approval and appreciation of President Coolidge's program of thrift and economy."

Some wag suggested it might prove embarrassing to appear in pajamas with a Pillsbury or Washburn-Crosby label stenciled across the toggery. No problem for President Cal, though. The companies producing the bags had perfected labeling that easily washed out.

Later, a Mrs. J.L. Murray of Bloomington, Illinois made a "wonderful colonial quilt" out of flour bags and sent it to Mrs. Herbert Hoover as an inaugural present. Mrs. Hoover was pleased. The Household Science Institute was so impressed with Mrs. Murray they gave her a job as a Field Extension Director.

While the greatest use of flour bags was in rural America, even society in the big cities was captivated by the idea. A magazine feature showed two attractive ladies lounging by the Fort Worth Country Club pool. One was wearing a one-piece suit made from four flour sacks. The other lady, featuring a two-piece suit, needed just a single one-hundred-pound striped feed sack for hers.

The livestock feed industry, seeing what a good thing the flour milling people had, started imprinting their bags with appealing designs. These were aimed at the tastes of the women on the farms. That's where most of the feed would go. The feed people were successful in their promotion efforts, but never approached the volume and interest achieved by the millers.

The cotton flour bags had a hundred or more uses in the home Bemis Bro. Bag Co. advertised. Bemis was a giant in the bag manufacturing business, furnishing bags to millers throughout the United States. Flour-sack fashions were a big thing for Bemis. Their sales picked up as flour sales increased and America dressed in their product.

Bemis ran an ad in milling industry publications with the slogan "The best bargain in good cotton cloth!" claiming that cotton flour bags "have a hundred or more uses in the home." Here is how they listed them:

Aprons	Clothes Pin Bag	Drying Fruit
Auto Covers	Cold Frame	Drying Seed
Bandages	Collar and Cuff Sets	Dust Cloths
Beach Coats	Combing Jackets	Feathers
Bean Bags	Cover for Bread or	Fishing Bags
Bedspreads	Cake	Fly Nets for Horses,
Bed Spring Cover	Cover for Clothes	Cows
Bibs	in Closet	Garment Covers
Book Covers	Covers for Meat	Hand Bags
Broom Covers	Crib Covers	Hand Holders—Hot
Card Table Covers	Curtains	Dishes
Chair Covers	Diapers	Handkerchiefs
Chair Cushions	Dish Cloths	Hooked Rugs
Chicken House	Dish Towels	House Dresses
Windows	Dolls	Ironing Board Covers
Children's Aprons	Doll Dresses	Jelly Strainers
Children's Bibs	Dresses	Lamp Shades
Cleaning Cloths	Dress Form Linings	Laundry Bags

Luncheon Sets	Quilts	Stuffed Animals
Mattress Covers	Rags	Suit Case Sets
Middies	Refrigerator Bags	Sun Suits
Mop Cloths	Rompers	Table Cloths
Muffin Covers	Sanitary Cloths	Table Covers
Pads for Stair Carpet	Scrap Books	Table Runners
Pajamas	Seeds	Toast Pockets
Partition Screens	Sheets	Tool Bags
Patches	Shirts	Tray Cloths
Picking Apples	Shoe Cases	Tree Bandages
Picking Nuts	Slings for injuries	Underwear
Pillows	Smocks	Vanity Table Drapes
Pillow Slips	Strainers for Lard	Waste Paper Bags
Pockets	Strainers for Milk	Yardstick Holders
Pot Cloths	Strainers for Paint	

It took the Australians to say in their inimitable way why it was important to do something about flour sacks. In the Norwestern Miller of May, 1926, the Australian Baker magazine was quoted: "Therefore, let us avoid the waste of used calico flour sacks. Let us invent some methods of using them after they have emptied their contents other than for washing the floor or stuffing up cracks in the walls. It should be much easier than finding uses for discarded politicians and safety razor blades."

The Americans had the answer. They created the flour-sack fashion industry and thereby brightened the American landscape for years to come.

The Mom Watch

In a small town there were no limits to your playground. The entire town was your field of activity. The town was that small. Everyone understood. Then how did moms keep track of the kids?

Easy.

The Mom Watch.

Every mom kept a watch on what was going on in her sight. And reported to the proper mom authorities if there was deviltry afoot or risks involved.

There were risk possibilities: climbing to the top of the town water tower, walking the top beam of the bridge over the river, playing Tarzan in tall trees, smoking Indian tobacco behind somebody's shed. These would get moms stirred up.

A summer day, or a Saturday during school months might go like this:

"Where ya goin' this afternoon, Skip?"

"I'm going over to Eddie's and then we're gonna go over to Bud's to see his new rabbits."

That was just the beginning. Before the day was over the gang would cover much more territory.

No problem for mom though. All she had to do was call a few moms and the network would quickly produce tracking that would locate the kids.

"Have you seen Skip?"

"Hi, Ruth. No, not for awhile. He was around here but I think the boys went in the direction of Hubbard's."

"Hello, Esther (Hubbard). Have you seen Skip and his pals?"

"Ruth, I gave them some cookies about an hour ago and they said they were going to check on some pet rabbits, but I also heard them say something about the lumber yard."

"John (at the lumber yard), have you seen that son of mine and his friends?"

"Oh, hello, Ruth. How are you? Say, tell that husband of yours that I sure would like to go fishing Friday night. I hear the Catfish are biting and the new stinky bait I just got should do the trick. What was that you said about Skip? Yeah, they're out back where we've got that scrap lumber pile. They asked if they could have some of that old stuff. Said something about building a shack. I told them to go ahead. Bye, Ruth."

The system was as good as a 14-jewel watch with a Swiss movement.

The army could have learned a thing or two about an intelligence network from the moms in a small town.

Moms and Dads

Moms. That's what they were called. Everybody had a mom. You hardly knew anyone whose mom was called mother. Too formal in a friendly, small town. There should have been an annual Mom's Day, but that didn't get invented until later and then they called it Mother's Day. If it had been small town folks putting that holiday together, it would have been called Mom's Day.

Not that there wasn't a mother or two in town—most often matronly types who liked the formality of the title and their grown-up kids obliged.

But it wasn't the norm.

Kids just plain felt comfortable calling mom mom. It seemed to make the kinship closer. It said love and respect in a warm way.

These were the things kids would say and mom sounds just right.

"Is my mom looking for me?"

"My mom really gave it to me yesterday for going out to the river without asking. It was something. Boy, was she mad."

"My mom is better than your mom." "No, she isn't, my mom is better than your mom." (This was never decided.)

"Your mom makes the best cookies in town. Think she'd give us some if we asked real nice?"

"Does your mom make you go to Sunday School every Sunday? Mine does."

"My mom and dad had a heckuva fight last night. I mean a real lollapaloozer."

"Let's ask mom if she'll take us fishing. I think she will. She likes to fish."

"Ya know, Susie's okay, but watch out if you go over to her house, her mom is hell on wheels."

Moms were something special.

What about dads?

Same thing.

There was only one father in town who was always called that. He was the priest at the Catholic church.

When it was your dad, father was too strong a title. It rang of authority, trouble, strong admonitions. Like when the school principal said, "I'm going to speak to your father about your conduct in school. You're going to have to straighten up or you are going to be expelled. This is my last warning."

It was dad you went fishing with. Dad you went hunting with in the big woods and along the river. Dad took you to the baseball games and bought you ice cream cones when you were little and a good baseball glove and bat when you got older.

Dads were special for daughters. Almost every daughter had her dad wrapped around her little finger and he loved it. They had a bond that would go on through life.

Moms and dads. A nice way to have it.

For the record, we all have mothers and fathers. It's on your birth certificate. But in the comfortable daily life of the family, it's moms and dads.

Just right.

Barefoot
On the Town

When you were in grade school you couldn't wait for the end of the school year. That final day as you left the school yard you had just one goal in mind.

Get home as fast as you can and get your shoes off.

Three months of glorious vacation going barefoot.

Shoes were never meant for kids, anyway. They were for grown-ups. Every kid wished he could live and go to school somewhere where you didn't have to wear shoes. You envied those kids in Africa in the *National Geographic*. They were in school and they weren't wearing shoes.

Girls and boys loved nothing better than getting up in the morning for another day of having fun without shoes. As a matter of fact, the shoes were out of sight. Usually under the bed or buried in back in the closet.

Every day wasn't a free foot day, though. Sundays you had to wear shoes to go to church and Sunday school.

This always meant a mad scramble, usually down on all fours, trying to find both shoes. One shoe was easy. Finding two shoes often was a problem. How they got separated and buried in different places wasn't explainable. It was just the way it was. Shoelaces were a problem, too. They seemed to disappear a lot. Girls had buckles. The boys had the missing shoelaces. Oh well, just pull your pants down over the tops of your shoes and nobody will notice.

Feet were tender when vacation started, but it didn't take long before they toughened up. Within a short time dirt and gravel roads, pastures (watch out where you step, there are horses and cows in here), the woods and the corn fields were comfortable to summer feet.

Bare feet had it all over tennis shoes or any other kind of shoes for most activities. Perfect for climbing trees, walking on roofs, pumping the swings in the school yard, wading in the creek, climbing in the hay mow.

There were rules, however.

It was okay to eat at the kitchen table barefoot. But you couldn't sit at the dining room table unless you had your shoes on and that was always on Sunday and sometimes during the week when there was a birthday to be celebrated or the pastor came to call.

You had to wash your feet every night when you came in from the day's play. Either under the pump out in the yard or in the big bucket or wash tub out in the back room off the porch.

While the happiest day of the year was the day school let out for summer and you went barefoot for the first time that year, an unhappy day was bound to come.

The first day of school in the fall, right after Labor Day, was the unhappiest day of the year. Your feet had to be encased for another nine months. You squeezed into shoes a little tight. Your feet had grown and they weren't used to shoes. They screamed to be free, destined to be prisoners for many months until released from confinement the next spring. The best you could do was slip the shoes off under your desk and hope the teacher didn't see you.

It took time, but in time your feet once again got used to shoes. You grudgingly accepted this condition, but vowed if you were ever elected President of the United States and in charge of running the country you'd make it a law that kids didn't have to wear shoes unless they wanted to.

That would be justice.

What You Did On a Summer Day When There Was Nothing to Do

Kids in small towns made the most of vacation days. They looked forward to the fun time of summer for nine months—nine of sitting and squirming at their desks and daydreaming about all the wonderful things they would do when the school bell rang for the last time at the end of the school year.

The first days of vacation were jammed with activity, a pile-up of things to do that had been stored in young minds during those long school months. Pent-up energy spilled out when school was over in May.

But as summer wore on the storehouse of ideas and energy emptied. Then came the days when there didn't seem to be anything to do.

Now the kids fell back on traditional activity. Not planned. Hardly thought of. Activity that sort of fell into place by itself. You could do it alone, with a buddy, with three or four pals. Could be a brother or sister mixed in. Pals were pals, male or female. One thing led to another.

You could:

Stop in at the butcher shop and see if "Butch" had some extra bones for your dog (or dogs).

Check the alleys back of the grocery stores for carrot tops and beet tops, slightly over-the-hill lettuce, and various other green items for your pet rabbits. The grocer didn't mind, in fact encouraged the kids to make good use of his refuse. Made for less carting away by the grocery.

Walk down to the elevator and check the railroad siding for spilled corn from the loading of grain cars. The corn was needed for pet pigeons. There were a lot of pet pigeons in town. Rabbits, too. And an assortment of other animals including several pet raccoons and a pet skunk made aromatically socially acceptable by the town vet.

Check building sites— new house, garage, barn— for a number of useful items: slightly bent nails, odd pieces of board, a bit of screen, panes of glass with a corner broken off, odd pieces of lath still okay for kite building, old shingles, throw-away pieces of linoleum just right for the floor of your dog's house.

Building sites were vital to a gang's ambitions. This is where the lumber came from for the gang's shack at the back of a vacant lot and hidden by trees. Not only building sites, but also wherever an old building, now past its useful days, was being torn down. Discarded pieces of board were perfect for building bird houses, bread boards for Christmas gifts, and dozens of other valuable items.

Hike to the newest road-tarring project and cut off fresh chunks of tar (cooled to just the right consistency) for chewing. Tar chewing went with summer.

Find the ice wagon. The ice man was always happy to let you catch the chips when he cut a big block. You couldn't beat sucking chips on a summer day when the thermometer was hovering close to the 100-degree mark.

"Walk the ties." A popular pastime was heading out on the railroad tracks to look for things dropped from passenger trains. You might find a coin or two rarely or almost any item carried by train passengers who were often bounced about in the openings between cars as they journeyed from one end of the train to the other. Empty whiskey bottles were plentiful but they were only good for throwing. A bonanza was finding a box of goods that had been jarred out of a boxcar when a door was accidentally left partly opened.

One kept one's eyes down while walking the ties, but not just because the ground was being searched. The game was to step only on the ties and see how many you could walk before your rhythm fell apart and you miss-stepped onto the gravel base. For some reason known only to railroaders, the ties were not spaced for normal, stretched-out walking; they were spaced at a distance that called for a shortened, prancing step. If you were really tops at this sort of thing you might count 500 ties before you "fell off." Have a couple pennies in your pocket to lay on the rails if a train came along. Flattened pennies made good trading material.

Take a route across town that included whatever fruit was ripe and ready for picking from friendly trees and stops at gardens that could produce carrots and juicy red tomatoes.

Trade. Anything. Two plain rabbits for a rabbit with color. Three or four mixed rabbits for a special "breed" rabbit. Pigeon for pigeon. Two pigeons for one fancy pigeon. Two rabbits and three pigeons for a pet raccoon. All kinds of marbles: a super aggie was good for four or five ordinary aggies. Two aggies would get you a big steelie. A jackknife, three aggies, a steelie and your best rabbit might get you a good hunting knife. And so it went. Endless.

Walk the ditches of the most-traveled roads searching for returnable bottles that the grocery store would accept.

An afternoon search that was successful could pay for a visit to the soda fountain.

Go fishing in the "crick." Mostly you caught Bullheads and not very big ones. Big enough to eat, though. Mom was not always happy to see the kids come home with a string of Bullheads but she dutifully got them to the skillet for supper.

Check the dairy on the North side of town and see if their new bull had been turned out with the cows. Could be interesting.

Tour the garages and see if any new cars had been shipped in. A new car at the Chevy or Ford garage was a special event in town.

Find out whose mom was baking cookies and find some excuse for stopping by, like "maybe you've got some chores that need doing Mrs. Jones."

The list of things you could do was endless. There was no schedule. Nothing was programmed. They were just there. Available. This was a kid's life. The life that made happy days go by.

All too quickly.

Snipes Anyone?

There was a time of the year, usually the balmy days of spring or Indian Summer, when Snipe hunting was at its peak.

No definite opening date to the season. Just when circumstances dictated it was time to go on a hunt.

Initiation of high school freshmen was one occasion. They were prime targets. Otherwise the hunt just happened anytime a dropped comment here and there indicated a potential "victim."

Now it was time to build enthusiasm. Create suspense. Talk about the excitement of the hunt. How it would be all the gang going in pursuit. Comrades for a night seeking the wily quarry. A sure fire "victim" was a newcomer to town who, it was determined by careful questioning, was from a place where the "sport" apparently wasn't practiced.

On the appointed date several of the gang were designated to pick up the "victim" at his home and pump him full of exciting ideas about the big night ahead. He was told about latest hunting reports and successes and where the scouting had indicated an area well populated with Snipes. This almost always was a distant woods or a lonely road way out in the country next to a corn field.

At least two car loads of hunters set out for the hunting grounds once dark began to descend, everyone carrying his gunnysack. Gunnysacks are what you caught Snipes with and you took turns being a "driver" or a "catcher." At least that's what you told the "victim." Fact of the matter is only one gunnysack would be used and you know who would be holding that gunnysack. But the illusion was maintained that everyone would be catching Snipes and a big haul was expected for the night's efforts.

At the appropriate place as night's darkness closed in the "victim" was placed at his post. He was instructed to keep his gunnysack open, close to the ground, to shine the flashlight he had been told to bring inside the bag to attract the Snipes and to emit low whistles every few minutes to entice the game into his trap. He could also "call in the Snipes." He was told Snipes were attracted to the human voice.

Snipes were variously described to him as furry, feathered creatures that could fly but usually ran at a very fast clip close to the ground. They were suckers, though, for that light inside the bag. They would be drawn to it as by a powerful force. The trick was to close the bag fast once one of them was inside. Couldn't take a chance of losing game once you had it in hand.

Meantime, the rest of the "hunters" had been dispersed around the area. They would either be posted or driving the Snipes toward our "victim." He was assured there'd be plenty of action. All the recent "hunting reports" emphasized that Snipe hunting was the best it had been in years.

The cars had left, ostensibly to go back to the starting point for the big drive. In reality, to pick up the gang and quietly slip back into town. After a Coke or a root beer, a lot of laughing and chuckling and, "wondering how our friend is getting along. Bet he's doing a lot of whistling," the gang broke up and all went home to bed. It was now almost 10 p.m.

Back at the Snipe grounds our lonely hunter waited patiently for the Snipes to run out into the open. He faithfully kept his flashlight burning and the mouth of the gunnysack open. Every few minutes he emitted a low whistle. And finally he resorted to a Snipe call: "Here Snipe, here Snipe, here Snipey." To no avail. Where had the Snipes gone? They said there were a lot of them this year. "I wonder how the other guys are doing?"

When did it dawn on our young friend that something was amiss? About two hours, maybe three, after nothing happened. No Snipes and the night was getting darker, it seemed, pitch dark, and a sharp chill began to penetrate.

Call out to the guys. No answer. Call the names of the "friends" who had picked him up at his house early in the evening. No answer.

With no response and after thoughtful review of the situation, there was nothing to do but start walking back to town. Maybe he would run into the guys and the cars.

No such luck.

Eight miles and tired feet later the lights of the town rose up in front of him. Our "victim" crept home, tired to the bone, and fell into bed. No Snipes. An unsuccessful hunt. Or was there such a thing as a Snipe? He wondered.

It was his first Snipe hunt and one he'd never forget.

There would be others, but next time he would be "one of the gang."

The Town Tavern

The town tavern was where you had a beer or a "hard drink," maybe played some cards or a little pool. A place where you met friends and talked about events of the day and complained about what went on in Washington.

But the tavern often was a lot more.

Business was transacted in the tavern.

It was headquarters for the town baseball team or softball team, or both.

A message center. Information was relayed through the bartender or posted on a bulletin board.

Hunting and fishing intelligence was collected at the tavern and dispensed to all.

An employment agency. Looking for a job? Check in at the tavern for leads. Want to hire somebody? Tack up a note and provide background on the job with the bartender.

The site of the public phone.

The billboard for every event within 20 miles. Wedding dances, fund-raising dinners, rod and gun club meetings, cribbage tournaments, baseball tournaments, high school sports schedules, farm auctions and town auctions. You name it, you could find it tacked up in the tavern.

Taverns were ticket agencies. They sold tickets for every good cause. Without this effort the annual Bullhead fry to raise money for the volunteer fire department probably would not have been successful.

The tavern was a social center for many. A home away from home for those who only had a lonely room waiting for them at the end of the day. This idea wasn't looked on favorably by some in the community, but it was a fact. You can't ignore facts. There were those whose only Christmas tree was the one in the corner of the tavern. All holidays found an atmosphere of festive cheer in the tavern.

There was a social service aspect, too. It was at the tavern that a collection was taken up to help the unfortunate when a neighbor's house burned to the ground, hospital bills from a devastating illness had made the family destitute, or, happily, money was needed to be raised to send the school spelling champion to Washington, D.C., for the national contest.

No gambling was allowed in the tavern. Cards were played for fun and as a test of skill. Get money involved you got trouble. That's what the tavern keeper always said. He was right. The same with pool. Oh sure, play for a beer or two. That was okay. But no more.

There was an air of excitement about the tavern. If you heard of something momentous happening you headed for the tavern to find out the details. Good or bad news.

Word of what might well be a record spread on antlers on a big white-tail buck would bring a group together in record time to hear the always colorful details of the hunt. Farm accidents, car accidents, fires, storms— all of these were verbal fodder for the tavern. After all, it would be days before the weekly Chronicle came out with the story and one wanted to know now what had happened.

In every community there were those who thought taverns were evil. Should be abolished. That argument was over, though. Prohibition had been repealed. The public wanted its taverns. Not all the public, of course, but the majority. The voters decided that.

But the tavern was fact of life. Some said an institution. That was stretching things a bit.

On the other hand, when you really took a close look at all the things that went on there and the good deeds accomplished, maybe you could say they were sort of special and valuable to the community.

Where Bullhead Was King

In many a small town in the Midwest and South, the Bullhead was the most popular fish—whether catching it or eating it.

There was a simple explanation. There were more Bullheads than any other kind of fish, they were easier to catch, and they filled lots of skillets.

The elite fish was the Black Bass. Found in the faster flowing water of a river or under overhanging trees in a quiet pool in the bend of the stream, this was the most sporting of fish. Hard to catch, though; took lots of skill and the right equipment, often luminous tandem spinners with red or brown feather tails. You had to get them to the frying pan pretty quick, though. The flesh tended not to stand up so well on a hot day.

Not so our good old Bullhead. That tough "hide" protected the meat from all elements for hours on end.

If the Black Bass was the elite fish, then the Catfish, especially the Blue Channel "Cat," was the gourmet dish.

Catfish were caught by rod and reel, trot line with a dozen hooks stretching across the river, or on a plain old cane pole dangled off a high bank, treble hooks packed with "stinky bait."

Catfish bait was always "stinky bait," made from concoctions of ingredients better not mentioned. There was always someone in town with a reputation as an "artist" of "stinky bait" creation. It was his "stinky bait" you wanted if you wanted to improve your chances of fishing success.

Most Catfish were caught at night so the most successful fisherman were those who could stay alert through the long, dark hours, rolling and smoking Bull Durham cigarettes or a pipe and drinking strong, black coffee boiled in a gallon can over a fire.

But it was King Bullhead who provided the majority of sport and fish dinners for folks. Bringing home 25, 50 or even 100 Bullheads was not unusual for three or four fishermen. So, there were always enough fish for your house and some of the neighbors. Trout, Salmon, Snapper, these were names of fish read about or heard about, but no one had ever eaten any of them. Of course, folks didn't travel much in those days so they weren't apt to try strange fish.

Not important; who needed more than a good meal of Bullheads? This was eating at its best.

Bullheads were caught on night crawlers. A supply of these and you were on your way. Back home with the catch, only two more utensils were needed. A sharp knife and a pair of pliers. The knife did its necessary work, the pliers pulled the tough hide off the fish.

A quick wash in cold well water then into the cast iron skillet where full strength butter was simmering. Most cooks rolled the Bullhead in flour and liberally doused the fish (unfilleted) with salt and pepper.

Served with fried potatoes and some dandelion greens (cooked with bacon and well sprinkled with vinegar) and maybe some fresh string beans from the garden, and you had a meal for a king— courtesy of King Bullhead.

The Bullhead was a money raiser, too. Many a volunteer fire department or community softball program has benefited greatly from an Annual Bullhead Fry.

Midwestern folks were so dedicated to the Bullhead that even if they traveled hundreds of miles to the great fishing lakes of Minnesota and Wisconsin, where the Walleye Pike was supreme and considered by many the "best" of fresh water fish, the dedicated "Bullheaders" would quit Walleye fishing in a flash if they ran onto good Bullhead fishing. Lake people up North thought these "Bullheaders" a strange lot since no one in the North ate Bullheads.

Oh well, to each his own.

Auctions Were
More Than That

Auctions in a former day were a lot more than someone disposing of worldly goods.

They were social events.

A gathering of the community, whether it be farm folks or the folks in town. Either way there always was a good sprinkling of the town's residents at a farm auction and country folk were well represented at an auction in town.

Everyone knew everyone at the auction. Rarely was there a strange face. There were no antique dealers. What people there were in that business at that time wouldn't even know an auction was taking place. The news was kept local. Handbills were scattered in a narrow band, since folks didn't want to travel more than 10 or a dozen miles, and the handbill was reprinted in the weekly Chronicle which had about a 10-mile radius.

Since the family holding the auction knew they would have a crowd of friends in their yard for the big sale, members of the family knew they would be busy serving coffee, lemonade and cookies. They were the hosts. It was their party.

No charge.

The food wagon, today a familiar commercial operation at auctions, hadn't been developed. Nor would it have been welcome then. Customs were different.

When your neighbors came to visit, you extended the hand of hospitality. The fact that it was an auction cut no ice. This was a social occasion as well as a selling occasion.

There was an atmosphere of nostalgia around an auction. The family holding the auction was moving out of the community, or giving up farming for retirement in town, or, sadly, the old homestead was being given up because someone had passed on. The widow or widower would be moving in with the kids or into smaller quarters. Perhaps an apartment above one of the stores along Main Street.

Folks came to the auction because they wanted to visit or maybe they saw something in the handbill they could use. They also came, particularly the ladies, because they wanted to own something that had been owned by their "selling out" friends. In the future the new owners would always refer to these items as "chairs from the old Smith place," or "the waffle glass bowl belonged to Mrs. Adams, you know."

The auction lists were endless, it seemed. And no matter how long, there was a final sentence that said "many more articles are to be sold."

The descriptions weren't always accurate. One auction ad described a piece of furniture as Chip and Dale.

In the country, livestock and machinery headed the auction bill, followed closely by grains and hay, then tools and, finally, the household goods.

The variety was endless:

Milk cows, a few choice beef critters, horses, a complete line of farm machinery, tractors, plow, cultivator, seed drill, manure spreader, wagons, disc, drag, side rake, water-cooled 1 cylinder gas engine, harness; then tools and such used on the farm including pitchforks, shovels, log chains, electric motors, platform scales, ropes and pulleys, and more; rendering kettle, cream separator, corn knives, nail kegs, kerosene lanterns, milk cans, egg scale and egg crates, and more.

At this point the auction lists for farm and town were much the same. Households were households and items in the country or in town tended to be the same:

Square oak table with 5 leaves and 6 matching chairs, sideboard cupboard, kitchen table, assorted kitchen chairs, 2, 5, 10-gallon crocks, Dexter washing machine (hand operated), Maytag washer runs by electricity, Victrola, flat irons, dishes, rugs, wash boiler and tubs, walnut Victorian spindle crib, high chair (family heirloom), quilt rack and quilts, canary bird cage with stand, coaster wagon, copper wash boiler, two commodes, trunk that came from Germany in the 1880s, Monarch kitchen range (good condition), Excell heating stove, two ladders, Last Supper picture, kraut cutter, pickle crock, buck saw, miscellaneous tools (including hammers, screwdrivers and saws), two Farm Bureau bowls, Red Wing pitcher and wash basin, 4-drawer chest, 3-drawer dresser, iron bed, single bed, double bed with walnut head and foot boards, oak rocking chair, horsehair sofa, wicker flower stand, floral teapot, spittoon, glass-front bookcase, milk glass candy dish, round frame with carved butterflies, fruit jars, canning equipment, meat cleaver, cast iron skillets, sewing cabinet, inner tubes, assorted nails, screws and bolts, upholstered side chair, upright piano, 2-pedal Singer sewing machine, beehive jug, cast iron kettle, Aladdin lamp, many knickknacks, and more.

When the auction was over and the family possessions had departed in the arms of 50 to a hundred friends, there was left an empty feeling only softened by a sizable amount of cash which promised a more leisurely life or a new start in another community.

The auction made good conversation around the community for a week or so and then was forgotten.

Forgotten because another auction was scheduled— for next week, Saturday.

Something to look forward to.

Fun With a
Flexible Flyer

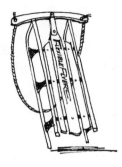

Boyhood in a small town in the Midwest had many joys, and sliding on winter days was one of them.

Not just your regular, down the hill sliding; there was something much better and more exciting.

But you had to be part of a special time to partake, and that time is a long time ago. Ah, but what memories.

Requirements were a very small town in the farm country, bobsleds drawn by teams of sturdy horses, and not letting mom or dad know what you were up to.

Saturday was the best day.

The farmers headed to town in the mornings, taking in a load of farm products, then buying supplies and heading back home. This went on throughout the day.

You waited at the edge of town, almost half a mile out.

Along came the bobsled, almost always driven by a familiar face.

You got ready with your trusty Flexible Flyer, then a short sprint, flop down, grab the top of the big back runner with the right hand, steer with the left hand to keep your sled on a parallel course and joy-ride into town, stopping just short of where the town marshal might be patrolling Main Street.

With four big runners, front and back, four of the gang could hitch a ride at the same time. It was quite a sight.

The ride was best when the friendly farmer put Maude and Old Bet into a good trot and the runners of your Flyer flew along on the packed snow.

You hung around in a bunch, talking about your ride, until bobsleds came along heading out of town. Then it was a reverse ride to the outskirts to catch another bobsled coming in.

What a glorious feeling.

What fun.

What adventure.

A small town special way of life. The last ride as the sun began to fade in the west was the end to a perfect day.

Twenty Things
You Could Do
With a Cigar Box

Kids in small towns could find no greater treasure than a wood cigar box. Sure, peach boxes were good to make airplanes— saw out the fuselage from the end of the box and make the wings out of the top pieces— but with a cigar box there were unlimited possibilities.

Cigar boxes usually were made of cedar and often came from exotic, faraway places like Cuba and Central America and South America. They had a pleasant aroma for months after the last cigar had been sold to a customer. That took time! Most men bought one cigar at a time. You could tell a wealthy man by how he bought his cigars— by the box.

The boxes had interesting decorations and names that conjured up the mysterious, the powerful, the rich and the rulers, national pride, ancient history. Names such as Dutch Masters, Antonio and Cleopatra, Garcia Vega, Muriel, House of Windsor, La Corona, Wm. Penn, Valdez, Hoyo De Monterrey, Rey Del Mundo, Royal Jamaica, El

Producto, Partagas, Cuesta Rey, H. Upman, Montecruz, Macanudo, Don Diego.

You kept an eagle eye on the counter at the drug store where the cigars were housed under glass, watching to see when a box soon would be empty. Getting in your request early was important, about the time the first cigar was sold out of the box. There was competition. Lots of kids, both boys and girls, wanted cigar boxes. Grown-ups, too. Sometimes you had to get in line. Good thing was there were lots of cigars smoked in earlier days and boxes emptied frequently.

Then the magic day would come. The last cigar would disappear out the drug store door with a customer leaving a trail of smoke. The box was yours.

Now, what to do with it. There were lots of choices:

A fishing tackle box.

A place to keep your marbles, especially your valuable aggies. The steelies were better kept in a cloth sack.

A valuables safe. The place for your rings, buckeyes, four-leaf clovers, booster pins, important papers such as agreements signed with pals.

Savings bank. Nail lid shut. Cut a slot in center of lid. Calculate the amount of money you would have if filled with pennies, nickels and dimes.

Cabinet for crystal radio.

Cash register for lemonade stand.

Tool box. Small tools, that is.

Stringed instrument. Remove lid. Use box as sound-ing box. Attach length of two-by-two for arm. String with catgut obtained from somebody's discarded instrument. Or, check with the music teacher at the school for broken

strings still long enough for your use (tie if necessary).
Makes a good ukulele.

Butterfly or bug collection box. Place cotton in bottom
of box to show off specimens.

Cage for very small pets. Fasten lid. Drill air holes in
top. Particularly good for critters that crawled or slithered
(like baby snakes). Only of temporary use for pets that
grew fast.

The perfect place for your rock collection.

Hideaway box for comics and certain paperbacks you
didn't want anybody to see. That is anybody except your
closest pals.

Incubator for hatching whatever you were hatching
this year. Keep near stove.

Lunch box.

Container for ammunition for your 22 or 410. Keep
on high shelf away from small kids.

Jewelry box.

A place to keep paper dolls.

A doll bed. Line the inside with felt or quilting. Remov-
ing lid optional.

School supplies kit. Ideal for pencils, pens, crayons,
rubber erasers, paper clips.

Baseball card file.

The list went on and on. As far as your imagination
and ingenuity could take you. Kid wealth could be determined by the number of cigar boxes owned— and filled
with important items.

A lot of things could disappear from your life over the years, but many a former resident of a small town (or a big town) with gray hair still had some of those same cigar boxes tucked away and filled with keepsakes.

A century salute to the cigar makers of the world from the kids of America. Thanks for thinking of us.

Bigfoot

Long years before reports of a "Bigfoot" in the Western mountains, a creature "part animal and part human", a small town in the Midwest had its own "Bigfoot."

He created a sensation, at least for this little community. For a long time, word of the "creature" really didn't reach the state capital where the state's biggest daily newspaper was published. Not until enough skepticism was generated that the news traveled and folks questioned what was going on. The word spread.

With good reason.

What was going on was a result of boredom. It was the middle of a long winter— February— when most days are so long and dreary you'd think of almost anything that would relieve the boredom. But up until this time, no one had ever thought of creating a "Bigfoot."

Arthur did.

He was bored. And he was a handy guy with wood and tools in his shop. He could build almost anything you wanted. Practical items to do the job. Better than Sears & Roebuck.

Fiddling around in his shop and thinking— bored you see— he decided to have a little fun with the town folks. He decided to make some giant feet out of wood. Carefully carved with his jackknife so they would be realistic.

The models were his own feet. There he was, sitting on a bench in the shop, barefooted, studying his feet and carving. Size? Very big. These wooden feet were bigger than anything known to man or primate. A size 9 was Arthur's size and he multiplied by three, so we are talking about size 27 or nearly 30 inches.

Some feet!

Like nothing ever seen before.

Then Arthur (remember he was bored until this idea gripped him) had a flash of genius.

He would make some strap fittings so his wooden feet could be walked in heel-to-toe or toe-to-heel. Both directions.

In other words, he could make imprints in the snow one direction and go back the opposite way with the feet still pointing in the same direction.

Confusing.

Scary.

Ingenious.

A week of diligent effort and the feet were finished.

What to do with them? The plot?

Arthur figured the best way to get the town excited was to visit a number of back yards where excitable folks lived, including several elderly spinsters whom he counted on to be in a state of terror the next day, telling everyone in town about the big footprints in the snow.

Arthur started his forays from well-traveled roads or well-used paths where regular footprints were plentiful and wouldn't mean anything.

Then he carefully slipped on the "feet" and crept up to bedroom and living room windows where "it appeared" he was peeking in at human life.

Was "Bigfoot" human?

Was he human and animal?

Was he a giant like the Cardiff giant that had been hidden in some woods or a deep valley for years?

What or who was this?

Well, as you can imagine, the entire town was talking the next day. A half-dozen homes had been visited by the creature who had then disappeared into his lair, wherever that was. (Arthur's shop, of course).

There was no more boredom in this small town. Everyone was excited. All a-titter.

In a later day, the news would have traveled fast. As it was, the news stayed in town. Until it was all over.

It took a little more than a week. The town began settling down after a few days and then Arthur slipped out into a dark night with fresh snow on the ground and visited more homes— a few repeats from the first excursion and a few new ones— bound to stir things up.

Just when the several elderly spinsters visited on the first "Bigfoot" night were nearly calmed down by old Doc

Jones, who liberally dosed them with his most potent "calmer", the creature was back and these and other ladies of the town were near panic. Some of the men, too.

Arthur knew it was time to quit.

It had been an exciting time.

The town's boredom was lifted.

He carefully and secretly burned the feet.

People talked the rest of the winter about "what this was." Man or beast, they wondered? Some suspected a hoax. Several of the elders of the town wondered if there wasn't a culprit in town.

As a matter of fact, Arthur was suspected. So were several others.

He just smiled when asked if he knew anything about "Bigfoot," or if he had an opinion. He said he didn't have an opinion.

The town talked about "Bigfoot" for years afterwards. Mostly after a big snow when some would apprehensively look to see if there were any new tracks.

Speculation took a hundred avenues, but the truth would never be known.

Arthur took it to his grave.

In his will he had requested that his favorite jackknife be placed in his pocket when he was buried.

How to Make
A Kite for Nothing

You could fly a kite almost anywhere in a small town.
Just look out for the trees. The school yard and the
football field were popular kite-flying centers as were
handy pastures at the edge of town.

There were manufactured kites. But they cost money.
Make your own. That was the idea. Save the money for
something else. Everybody built kites. It was fun. There
was competition to see who could make the best kite and
whose kite would fly the highest and the best.

Some constructed box kites or made dragon kites.
Adults got involved here, but when it came to kite building
and kite-flying, adults were kids. You never got too old to
fly a kite.

Mostly, though, the kids made their own kites. And for
nothing.

Here's how it was done:

1. Obtain two laths from the lumber yard or the nearest house project. It wasn't necessary to "borrow" the laths. If you told the construction boss or the lumber yard manager what you wanted the laths for he always found a few extras you could have. Keep the laths full length for a regular kite. Cut the laths to 25 inches if you wanted a small kite.

2. Make paste with flour and water. Some people added a dash of salt but no one knew why.

3. Take four newspaper pages, double them, two for the front side of the kite, two for the back side.

4. Nail the two laths together in approximately a cross position. Use both nails and glue for maximum strength.

5. Use strong cord, obtained from your friendly hardware dealer or your dad's shop, to attach to the four ends of the laths, making a frame on which to hang the paper.

6. Fold paper over cord and glue.

7. Punch two holes where laths cross. This is where you tie your kite line. Paste extra layers of paper around and over this area to prevent ripping.

8. Make tail from strips of rags. Tie rags together to make at least 15 feet of tail. Select rags from mom's rag box to achieve a colorful tail.

With 50 to 100 yards of kite string you are ready to fly your kite. Kite string can be any combination of strings tied together but the longer the sections the better. Use a "winding board" to hold string.

A good kite-flying wind was all that was needed. Goal was to see who could fly a kite highest, who could make the most spectacular dives and climbs, and who could stay up the longest. If you were bold you tied your kite to a fence post and left it up all night.

Cost of kite: Nothing.

Satisfaction: Total.

Result: Great kite-flying as long as the paper and glue held together.

No problem, though. If your kite crashed and left only a pile of wreckage you could make a new kite in an hour.

And it wouldn't cost a penny.

The Last Days
Of the Medicine Man

The Medicine Man lasted on the American scene, in the really small towns, into the early 1930s.

We're talking here about the old-fashioned Medicine Man, not the latter day dispenser of bottled goods who used a big bus road show and modern advertising to sell his concoction.

Medicine Men had been around since the Colonies and their last stronghold was the small towns of the Midwest and the South. It was in these small towns that folks, the older ones, still believed in elixirs they had consumed for years after buying them through the mail, or from the back of a Medicine Man's wagon.

What the Medicine Man brought to town was entertainment, some excitement, and salesmanship through a gift of gab unparalleled for the sick in the audiences. Good feelings pervaded the community after a visit of the Medicine Man since the biggest percentage of the tonic was good old alcohol, or corn whiskey, white lightning, or whatever substance was at hand and could be mixed with sweet syrups to make the final product.

The entertainment more often than not was an elderly Indian (or a good replica from some Mediterranean background) who wore the feather headdress, beat a drum to attract the crowd and, carrying a smaller drum and beating it, danced the dances of his "Indian ancestors." The first Medicine Man wagons were horse-drawn and they continued this way even after Model T's and trucks were available.

More romantic, you see.

The horse disappeared in the 30s and that was the beginning of the end of the Medicine Man, truly one of the great characters of his time.

What kind of man was he? Well, P. T. Barnum and Buffalo Bill Cody would be his "first cousins". He really never conned anyone, never cheated—just sold his bottles for crisp $1 bills. Smaller bottles went for 50 cents when he was finding sales resistance to the "giant-size" bottles.

He always checked in with the Mayor and the town Marshal when he arrived in town.

Gave each of them a complimentary bottle of "Dr. Smith's Miracle Remedy." That did it. Everything was just fine from that moment on.

Those of the legal medical practice frowned on these "goings on," but there was no use keeping the townsfolk from their fun and no real harm would come from a little hooch disguised as remedy "for all one's ills."

Plus that it had been a long time since an Indian had danced on Main street.

Long May It Wave

Three times a year the populace of small towns turned out to fly the flag high, salute our country's heritage, pay respects to fallen heroes, and make a lot of noise.

Just about everybody who could walk took part in the Fourth of July celebration and the events surrounding Decoration Day, Flag Day and Armistice Day.

If you were old enough to carry a little flag, you marched in the parade. On the Fourth it ended at the city

park where speakers mounted a specially erected platform to bring the message of our independence to the assembled. The school superintendent led everyone in the pledge of allegiance, the mayor reminded all that the ancestors of those who founded the town had their roots in the Revolutionary War, and the speaker of the day, a locally prominent politician, recited all the reasons America was the greatest land on earth.

It was always hot on the Fourth. Fans waved everywhere, rippling across the park like waves on a lazy sea. Fried chicken, potato salad, and watermelon was the menu of the day. The parade to the park was timed to end about 11 a.m., just in time to settle down in a shady, grassy spot, lay down a blanket and spread out the Fourth of July picnic dinner. Somehow, the speeches sounded better if you were enjoying a good picnic meal.

The parade was the most colorful part of the day. In the 1920s and the1930s, many of these had a Civil War veteran as the Grand Marshal. His presence brought history and its agonizing conflicts close to everyone present. The color guard and the rifle squad were made up of World War I vets who could still get into their uniforms. Some towns had a Spanish-American war veteran who added special color to the occasion, but not many. It just wasn't a big enough war to provide vets for all those towns.

Music was provided by the town band. Not really a marching band, its members tried their best to keep in step while playing the popular marches. The music was fine. Out of step wasn't all that important.

Everyone was up at dawn on the Fourth. There wasn't any choice. Kids, who had looked forward for days to this celebration, started setting off firecrackers with the first light despite the pleas of parents who would liked to have slept in on this holiday. No chance. The young ones were up and out of the house and down the street with their ammunition before they could be stopped.

Little kids had to be content with sparklers and very little firecrackers lit only with mom and dad's help.

But the bigger ones? Out of their way. They had plans for mighty explosions. It was the only way to celebrate our independence won on the battlefields of our country against the oppressive English. Those guns fired for our freedom had to be emulated with the biggest explosives legitimately called fireworks.

Torpedoes were thrown like bombs. Whole packages of small firecrackers (40 to 50 with their fuses intertwined) were lit to sound like a machine gun going crazy. But the big guns, the really heavy artillery, were the 2-inch, 3-inch and 4-inch cannon crackers. They went off with a mighty BOOM. Stand back, folks. These are dangerous. Light one and run for safety or light one and give it a good heave.

A tradition with the big firecracker shooters was setting off the 4-inchers under cans and seeing how high you could blast them. The idea was to set these off in the alley behind Main Street or in an adjacent street and see if you could send the cans soaring above the store rooftops.

It was a tough day for the town marshal and the captain of the volunteer fire department. They had to see that things didn't get out of hand and no fires were started because of firecrackers thrown in the wrong place.

It was just plain hell for the dogs of the town. Occasional bursts of firecracker fire from overanxious types before the Fourth told the canines it was coming. The dreaded day. It wasn't just the noise. Firecrackers were thrown in every direction. Not safe for four-footed creatures.

The fact is, you couldn't find a dog in town on the Fourth. They were out of sight, in or under anything that would hide them from view and muffle the noise of thousands of explosions during the long day.

There was a break in firecracker action for the parade, the picnic (you had to eat) and the beginning of the speeches. But that was enough. Back to the front. Load and fire. Celebrate our independence.

At night the festivities ended with Roman candles and skyrockets fired from launchers homemade from drain pipe and roof rain gutters. Who could forget the skyrockets bursting overhead with their colorful stars and streamers. A perfect end to a perfect day.

Decoration Day and Armistice Day were important observances. Parades, picnics and speeches, including recitation of Lincoln's Gettysburg Address by the star sixth-grader, were the usual. On Decoration Day the parade ended at the cemetery where there was the rifle salute to those who fell in our country's wars. It was the time when the community paid its respects to family long laid away. Their graves were decorated with fresh flowers.

Armistice Day was a military day. Everyone who could struggle into a uniform was expected to be in line. The Ladies Auxiliary of the American Legion marched in uniform. Every kid in town who could walk was in the parade. It was important to be a flag carrier. The parade ended in time for the crowd and dignitaries to be in place for the moment of silence that marked the exact minute the great war had ended in Europe. It was a solemn, moving occasion, never forgotten if you were one of the boys or girls in those parades.

You were proud to be an American. The best country in the world. Fought for and won by valiant men who dreamed of a better world in a free country.

America The Beautiful.

The Great
Can Kick
Record

To the town's recollection one of its youths, "Coffee" by nickname, held the world record for can kicking in the 1930s.

No one knows when Coffee got the idea to do a record can kick. There wasn't any Guinness Book of World Records then to offer a challenge. The local library, housed in widow Adam's house, didn't have any information on can kicking. It wasn't a regular sport and it wasn't listed under hobbies.

According to local history, the big event took place on a Saturday morning.

A Saturday morning when there wasn't anything special going on in town.

A fella had to think of something worthwhile to do.

That's when Coffee decided to kick that No. 2 tomato can.

Coffee started at the Northeast corner of town, at the old Duncan farm.

This was a street event. The route went down the East side of the school house, down Main Street to the library corner, then North by the library (Mrs. Adam's house), angled Southwest down Cloyd's Hill, and wound up at the Boydens, the last house before the road took you out of town.

Coffee then turned back towards Main Street in a more or less Easterly direction with a little South thrown in.

Arriving at the bottom end of Main Street, Coffee turned up Main Street and headed for his starting point.

By this time the word was out that a record-breaking competition was happening in town.

Quite a few folks came out on the sidewalks along Main Street to cheer Coffee on.

This was exciting.

This was news in the making.

With applause and cheers ringing in his ears, Coffee bent to his task, increased the pace and headed for the finish line.

All the way back to the old Duncan farm.

It was over. He was tired. His right big toe was sore.

It wasn't just kicking the can that caused that big toe to be sore. Sometimes he missed the can with his kick and moved a few rocks in the gravel street.

Along the way the "official observers" had kept track of all the variations from a straight line. Whoever heard of anyone kicking a can in a straight line? Impossible.

The final calculation was 7.8 miles, about 2.8 miles of that amount coming from the wandering back and forth across the streets.

The big event was written up in the next week's Chronicle: LOCAL BOY SETS CAN KICKING RECORD/FIRST EVENT OF ITS KIND IN THE COUNTRY.

The Chronicle said it had to be a world record since there was no record anywhere of a world record.

In any case it would always be a town record.

Coffee was a local hero. Folks talked about the Great Can Kick for more than a week.

Coffee was proud of his accomplishment.

When asked why he did it, he said, "Well, there wasn't anything else to do that day."

Whatever happened to that famous No. 2 tomato can?

The last anybody knew Coffee had it full of nightcrawlers and was going fishing.

The Social Scene

Most of the social life in small towns went back and forth between houses. Birthdays, baptisms, confirmations, weddings were major occasions for getting together. So was Sunday. It was tradition. You went to somebody's house for Sunday dinner or they came to your house.

The holidays were the high social events of the year. Thanksgiving, Christmas and New Year's were a parade of coming and going for weeks. Sometimes you had two or three stops to make in one day. By January 2 you had put on an extra 10 pounds and you had to worry about how to get it off.

Evening social times mostly were two or three, or even four, couples getting together to play cards. The old fashioned card games, that is. There weren't many bridge players in those days—except in the city where it was fashionable. Rummy or Canasta, Hearts, Whist—those were the kind of card games that were popular.

If it was a quilting bee the women gathered around the "work" stretched out in the parlor while the men sat around the kitchen table and talked about the price of corn, what a fat steer would bring in Chicago, latest planting ideas from Earl May or Henry Field down in Shenandoah, Iowa where they had two of the biggest seed companies in America and promoted sales on their own radio stations, the problems of the town council, and when they would improve the roads and maybe put in some paving.

Folks marked their calendars for the events at the school—grade, junior high and high school. No one missed any of these special times except maybe the ladies didn't go to the football games when there was snow on the ground in November. Every class, grades 1 through 12, put on an open house for parents, relatives and friends. Then there was a spate of musical presentations by the various instrumental and vocal groups. Two or three plays were offered in the gym/auditorium by the Drama Club. School days were busy days.

Boys and girls started becoming young men and young women at Epworth League, Christian Endeavor, Luther League and Catholic Youth. Dressed up because it was a church activity, but also because you wanted to look as good as you could to the other sex, you absorbed the lessons during a Sunday evening, listened attentively to the speakers, and anxiously awaited the social hour opportunity to talk with the boy or the girl you had your eye on. If you were bold—worked up enough courage—you asked the girl if you could walk her home. It was dating under the best auspices. It was co-education with the church's blessing. You couldn't beat that.

Many a marriage evolved from those Sunday evenings at the church.

Street dances were once or twice a year. Nearby towns also had street dances so you could easily get in a half-dozen or so during the summer if dancing was your thing. For many it was. It took a lot of corn meal on the paving, though, to effectively glide up and down and around the street to the beat of one of the local dance bands. The dances were festive occasions usually sponsored by the merchants during the annual carnival, the Fourth of July, or at harvest time. The biggest expenditure, outside of hiring the band and buying a few sacks of corn meal, was stringing the colored lights across the street over the dance area. Since the dances traditionally were on Main Street (after it was paved) the colored lights could be stretched between buildings. It was a colorful scene.

There was an annual box social at the school. The ladies vied to have the fanciest box which always featured delicious fried chicken. Also enough delicacies, including both cake and cookies, to make the box bulge. You made sure your husband or boy friend was ready to bid on your box if someone else didn't. High school boys and single men of the town were expected to enthusiastically bid on the single teachers' boxes. The proceeds went to buy band music or sponsor young talent at the state declamatory contest. The annual box social was a spirited event with a well-fed conclusion.

The American Legion was strong in small towns. Just about every town of any size had a Post. The Legion put on several dinners a year—all you could eat for 75¢—with dancing afterward. During the winter the Post sponsored Bingo nights with valuable prizes such as Faribault blankets, Red Wing pottery, 48-pound sacks of Pillsbury flour, and slabs of Rath's Blackhawk bacon.

Ladies' Aid was a number one activity of the town's women. Different churches called it by different names but the purpose was the same. Farm women came to town when they could get away to join their town counterparts at these meetings. Usually they were held in homes with the hostess on her mettle to provide the most delicate, delicious cookies and cake she could, plus tea and coffee. The level of excellence was observed closely. At the end of every session the ladies always said "that's the best cake (or cookies) I've had in I don't know when." This was repeated the very next meeting at the house of the next hostess.

They never admitted it but churches competed. Which pastor delivered the best sermons? Who had the nicest altar, the most talented choir, best soloist? It went on and on. The showcase competitions, though, were the annual church suppers. Every church had one. Premium social events. Everyone in town was invited. Most came. The ladies of the church planned and planned, cooked and cooked, baked and baked. No question about it, highlight eating of the year was the church suppers. Somehow things worked out and the churches took turns getting the most plaudits for their culinary excellence. After all, the townsfolk wanted to keep everyone happy— and keep those church suppers coming.

The lodges and fraternal organizations were prominent in many small towns, among them the Masons, the Royal Neighbors, the Moose and the Redmen. Some sold life insurance. Insurance was part of the fraternal bond. All of them sponsored annual social events and actively solicited new membership.

At the top of the social ladder was the D.A.R. You had to be descended from a soldier in the Revolutionary War to belong. Trouble was the records were too vague and information so difficult to uncover, most women didn't know whether they had any family in the war for independence. Those who did have the evidence and were duly admitted to the exalted ranks were wont to look down on the unqualified. Sad was the elderly lady who found out through a researching relative that she had heroes of the Revolution as the founders of her family in America and she would have been No. 1 in the local D.A.R. On the top rung of the social ladder. Looked up to. She could have carried the flag of the D.A.R. in the local parades. But it was too late. It wasn't that important anymore. Let somebody else run the show. The D.A.R. was bound to die out anyway. The young folks just weren't that interested. The ranks would thin. There were new things in life to think about, new ways. Times were changing.

The Depression had its effect on the social scene. Times were hard and there wasn't an extra penny for entertainment. Pot luck was the only way to have a get-together. Everybody share. Bring your favorite dish and have a good time. Plenty of coffee, lemonade for the kids and home brew for the men. Home brew was the least expensive way to have a drink during the Depression. It varied from good to fair to not so good. It depended on who made it. Some had the talent. Drink theirs. Some didn't have the knack for concocting the stuff. Pass theirs up. Go for the lemonade.

Folks did all sorts of things to get along during these tough times. Ingenuity often came into play as ways were found to have an enjoyable occasion on the little one had.

One group of seven families worked out a "wheel schedule." The families gathered every Sunday for dinner. Each family brought whatever the wheel said they should bring for that Sabbath day. It worked like a charm. All ate well and using the wheel meant you only had to bring the expensive meat once every seven weeks while enjoying seven Sundays of plain but delicious fare. After the big buffet feed for 25 to 30 the parents sat around and talked or listened to the radio while the kids played games. It was a perfect answer to beating the Depression and its limitations.

Small towns were a far cry from the big towns and the cities when it came to social life. There weren't the fancy balls, lavish dinners, and special entertainments of the city, but small town folks never complained.

How much more select could you be than your little community where everybody knew everybody and your friends were as many as the population of the town. It was the best of all situations and you wouldn't trade it for anything.

Going to
The Movies

Cultural opportunities in a small town weren't numerous, but there were enough. There was always something going on, especially in the summer when warm weather made outdoor attractions comfortable.

Going to the movies was a popular pastime. The feature changed every week with a bonus extra film at the Saturday matinee. This meant you could see 52 feature films a year and lots of folks did. They always had a night a week open for the movies.

First there were the silents with Jimmy the piano player providing the theme music up front. Then came the talkies. But not until long after the big towns had them. Small towns changed over much later. For good reasons. No hurry. Everybody loved the old silents. Mainly, though, it was the cost. Costs lots of money to change over to the talkies. It finally happened when residents began staying home out of protest. They wanted the new talking films everybody was talking about. Al Jolson in

"The Jazz Singer" had ushered in a brand new world of entertainment.

They had seen the stars of silents. Now they wanted to see and hear Douglas Fairbanks, Mary Pickford, Rudolph Valentino, Harold Lloyd, Fatty Arbuckle, the Marx Brothers, and the Barrymores.

Saturday matinees (10¢ admission) were something special. Every boy and girl in small town America grew up going to the picture show Saturday. No birthday parties were ever scheduled at that time. It was sacred to the kids. Their special hours. Escape to the wonderful world of film with all its magic. Typically, there was a newsreel, a comedy short, a short feature, the newest chapter of the serial "cliff hanger" that went on for weeks and weeks and usually a full length feature.

The feature at least ninety percent of the time was a cowboy picture. It was the heyday of William S. "Bill" Hart and his horse "Fritz," Ken Maynard and "Tarzan," Buck Jones and "Silver," Bob Steele, Harry Carey, Sr., Tim McCoy, and the great Tom Mix who made many pictures with his horse "Old Blue" before the days of his most famous horse, "Tony", the favorite of every kid in America.

These were the classic cowboy stars of an era not seen again until a later day when John Wayne picked up the mantle. Nope, the times they were "achangin'," someone said. He was right. Along came a cowboy movie actor with a guitar. A singing cowboy. Never heard of before. Oh sure, once in awhile a cowboy might sing a little in a picture but not carry his guitar and sing all the way through the show. Why, you'd think that guitar had replaced the six-shooter. Regardless, Gene Autry was a big hit. He was the new cowboy matinee idol, to be followed by Roy Rogers and Rex Allen. The times sure were "achangin'."

Movie house operators, always looking for a way to fill the seats, came up with a variety of promotions to attract the public.

Mystery Night had a 10¢ admission for everyone, 15¢ off the regular adult fare. The mystery was the movie itself, a secret until it came on the screen. No wonder. Few if any would have come if it had been advertised. It happened because the operator got it from the distributor at less than bargain basement cost. Other attractions included cash bonus night with $15, $10 and $5 drawings. A lot of money in those days. Dish nights were popular with several sets of "china" being given away during an intermission just before the feature.

Not all small towns had a regular movie theater. But they had movies. Usually, the local businessmen's club sponsored outdoor movies in the summer. A side street off Main Street was barricaded one night a week, a big screen erected, folding chairs or benches lined up and the free movie began at dark. It was great for all. The family came early to get a good seat. The merchants kept their stores open because happy moviegoers would stop in and do a little shopping before or after the movie. The grocery stores did a big business selling barrel candy for the kids. Every kid had to have a sack of candy on movie night. There was popcorn, too. But this was popped at home and brought in a big sack, enough for the entire family.

Only rain could dampen these occasions and most folks were willing to sit through a sprinkle or a light rain to see the show. It took a downpour to rout folks from their seats. Then they would crowd into the stores and wait out the rain. If it quit within an hour or so everybody returned to their seats and the show went on.

Band Concerts, Revivals and Other Cultural Events

Band concerts were standard entertainment in small town America. Any town worth its salt had a town band. Something to be proud of. A tradition. Anyone who could play an instrument halfway decent was eligible to join. If Tommy got a clarinet and had some lessons he was ready for a white shirt, a black bow tie and a seat in the band. The ages of the band members ranged from 8 to 80. Continuity was there. The old helped the young. The up and coming generations would take over.

So the band didn't always play exactly right. So what if somebody hit a wrong note, was off key. The general sound was just fine and it was loud enough for all to hear— up and down Main Street, around the square. Why, you could sit on the front porch five or six blocks away and hear the music just fine on a clear, summer night.

Folks looked forward to the weekly band concerts. Farmers drove in from the country and combined some shopping with the enjoyment of the concert. They parked their cars close to the bandstand so they could sit in comfortable car seats and have a front-row view of the players. Some folks in town, to ensure themselves of one of the best spots for sitting and listening, would drive their cars downtown early, several hours before the concert, walk home and have supper and then return in time for the first rendition.

The members of the band could tell if they were appreciated, if they were having a successful evening, by both the applause and the horn honking. A lot of noisy, prolonged horn honking meant audience acceptance and enthusiasm. The Stars and Stripes Forever always got the most honking.

Folks never could get enough of good band music. They heard John Philip Sousa and Karl King and other greats on the radio, but it wasn't like being right there, a few yards away, and hearing that music for real.

The band practiced early in the week for the concert, usually Monday nights. The practice room was on the second floor over one of the stores, like the big vacant room over the bank. Windows were kept open to cool things off and let a little fresh air in. Many of those practices were during evenings when the temperature struggled to get below 90 degrees. It was hot. There was a plus, though, for the music lovers of the town. They could come downtown and listen to the band practice. And many did. It beat sitting home and swatting flies.

Revivals were special. They were special because they were unscheduled and you never knew when a traveling revival preacher would be coming to town with his tent to save souls and drive evil from the community. Not that the regular preachers in the churches weren't doing their job. It was just that the evangelist types with their fiery oratory, exhortations and vivid verbal creations of hell and heaven were like nothing you had ever heard before. It was quite a show.

These traveling ministers of gospel could always count on enough unchurched and curious to fill most of the benches in the tent the revival minister and his helpers (family) erected in a vacant lot at the edge of town. He also could count on regular church-going folks who felt it was their duty to witness what this man was doing so they could report back to their congregations. It wasn't always necessary, however, since many of their friends would be filling the same benches. Doing their duty. Seeing what this was all about. Be ready to do something about it if this traveling preacher got out of line.

The money that went into the revival team's offering plates was money that wouldn't be in the town's churches. There was concern about this. But not too much. There was enough to go around. And the revival meeting had been worthwhile. The music alone was worth every penny you put in the plate. That preacher's wife and his daughters had the prettiest singing voices the town had heard in a long time.

Two weeks of the revival was usually enough to save everybody in town worth saving and then the tent was folded up and it was on to the next town. Had to get a lot of towns up North covered before bad weather set in. Then it was time to head for Southern communities.

Biggest of all was the Chautauqua. The phenomenal growth of this movement in America put Chautauqua in reach of just about everybody. Really small towns weren't big enough for a Chautauqua visit, but the County Seat town was and that's where you went because you wouldn't want to miss this experience even though it sometimes meant taking plenty of extra time with the Model T and probably getting home late at night.

Lecturers on every subject, talks by explorers, oratory by political leaders, and a large variety of entertainment by talented musicians: singers, instrumentalists in every combination from soloists to trios, quartets, quintets, and even choruses. The stars of entertainment from out of town often were augmented by locals who had achieved musical acclaim in their communities. This was their chance to appear with national musical stars and it made the community proud.

An evening at Chautauqua was an evening to remember. And it was all for the good, they said. Chautauqua was uplifting, enlightening, educational. It stimulated both the mind and the soul. Made you feel good about life, about the vast world revealed to you by those on the stage. There was nothing like it.

The town depended on the high school for most of the rest of its culture. During the school year the public was invited to several plays put on by the Drama Club, band and orchestra concerts by the junior high and senior high musical organizations, and an auditorium presentation by talented youths on their way to the state music contest.

And don't forget the town library. It wasn't big, but there were plenty of good books and classic literature to read.

Culture was an important aspect of small town life.

Overnight
On the River

There were rituals as a part of growing up in a small town. Proving you could smoke Indian tobacco was one of them even if the burning, bitter taste hardly made it worthwhile.

You took your first sip of corn whiskey obtained from the town bootlegger when you were just a teenager. A swallow or two was enough. You could talk about that for months. Brag a little. Even if you didn't like the stuff and probably would stay away from it for years. Good thing, too. Homemade corn liquor was not considered a healthy drink.

Going to a grown-ups dance at the lake side pavilion for the first time said you were an "adult" for sure. You maybe danced once or twice either with your sister, a cousin or somebody from the neighborhood and then hung around in the corner talking with your pals until it was time to go home.

Getting the car for the evening was a big step into

manhood. You'd been driving since you were 11 or 12, but you didn't get the car for the evening until you were legal age. Fourteen was young enough. The ritual for that first night with the car was to pick up your girlfriend for an early evening spin, let her off at her home early and then round up the guys for a joy ride out in the country. Test the old car. See how she would take the corners. Cross the controls into a gravel-throwing skid in a wide turn. Push her all the way up to sixty. Wow! That's about all the old road would take.

Then there was the great out-of-doors. The middle of the summer was the time for an overnight on the river. Borrow a pup tent, roll up some old blankets, talk mom into half a pound of bacon wrapped in wax paper and her old frying pan, the one the folks used on their camping trip to Yellowstone National Park, half a loaf of bread, your Boy Scout mess kit, a jelly jar of coffee and a quart coffee can to make it in, a couple of apples and you were on your way.

Hiking to the river was a part of it. No rides accepted. Everything was rolled into packs slung over the shoulder. Two to three hours of brisk walking brought you and your pal to the river bank. Best to find a good, dry sandbar. Less bugs there and sand is softer than ground baked hard by the mid-summer sun.

Build a fire. What's a camp without a campfire. Put on some coffee and drink the strong brew, dipping in folded slices of bread for a snack. Looking into the flames produced stories as imagination took hold. Roll up in your blankets in the pup tent and go to sleep listening to the crickets and small critters stirring around in the bushes.

Up at dawn, coffee, bread and bacon and all set for a day of fishing. Poles first as you tried for Catfish and Bullheads. During the heat of the day you could carefully wade along the shore and feel with your feet along the mud banks where fish might be hiding to cool off. They were logy from the heat and a quick grab could net you a two-pounder.

This was the challenge, you see. You hadn't brought anything to eat during the day since you had to prove yourself by catching enough fish to satisfy hearty young appetites. You hardly ever failed. With bacon greasing the pan and Catfish frying on a river bank, the day was perfect. Who could ask for anything more? It even made you forget the mosquitoes that had pestered you during the night and left a lot of lumps on arms, legs and neck.

Home by dark. Mission accomplished. Ritual observed.

The 1 ¢ Sale

Many little towns had a Rexall drug store. They were fine, honest operations, but so were other drug stores. What made the Rexall drug store special and different was the annual REXALL 1 ¢ SALE.

This was no ordinary sale, this was a community event. Of course, there wasn't all that much in the way of special events in towns of this size so anything that was exciting and different merited major attention from townfolk and those who lived in the surrounding countryside.

The Rexall genius who thought up the 1 ¢ sale has to be in the company's Hall of Fame. If he isn't, he should be. And, he should have profited handsomely from bonuses because there wasn't anything like it anywhere and it was always a success.

A sure-fire winner.

Everyone benefited. The drug store owner made buckets of profits. All the other merchants benefited because the 1¢ sale brought lots of people downtown or into town and they took in the other stores to see what specials they might have. They had them. You don't want to miss an opportunity like this, the storekeepers said.

The big sale days were advertised well ahead of the dates and the store itself was plastered with sales posters and placards describing items and the fascinating fact that for just 1¢ more you could get the identical piece of merchandise for which you paid the full price.

The weekly newspaper ads were spread out on the kitchen table where the entire family poured over the bargains to be had.

There was something for everybody.

But not everything was for sale for 1¢ when you bought the first item at the regular price.

Pocket watches and wrist watches weren't "on the sale." Neither was jewelry, or desk lamps, wallpaper, gift items since many were one of a kind, scissors, cooling fans, and anything the pharmacist had to mix up from his myriad of jars and cans.

Over the counter remedies were popular 1¢ sale items: Puretest Rubbing Alcohol, 2 pints for 51¢; White Pine and Tar Cough Syrup, 2 for 51¢; One Minute Headache Tablets, 2 for 26¢; Chloroform Throat Lozenges, 2 for 26¢; Epsom Salts, 2 for 16¢. You could get two bottles of Peptona— an efficient Iron and Nux Vomica for improving the appetite and for simple amnesia— for $1.01.

The ladies loved the 1¢ sales for the toilet goods: Bouquet Ramee Face Powder, 2 for $1.01; Georgia Rose Vanishing Cream, 2 for 26¢; Theatrical Cold Cream, 1 pound tins, 2 for 76¢; Dainty Deodorant, 2 for 36¢; Cream of Almonds, 2 for 26¢. For the men there was Rexall Shaving Cream, 2 for 26¢; Harmony Shaving Lotion, 2 for 51¢; and Petroleum Hair Rub, 2 for 51¢.

The list varied every year. Some years the school notebooks, jars of peanuts, fancy toilet soaps in boxes of two or four, chewing tobacco, pencil boxes, and crayons were "hot sellers." And, who could resist: Liggett's Sweet Milk Chocolate Bars, full-pound bars of Sweet Milk Chocolate enjoyed by young and old, this sale 1 bar 20¢, 2 bars for 21¢. For the tots there were Candy Wafers, assorted, 1 package 5¢, 2 packages 6¢. For the entire family: Symonds Inn Cocoa, invigorating and healthful beverage, 20¢ a can, 2 cans for 21¢.

The sale was like a big party. The drug store was filled with customers with their lists of items they wished to purchase and then receive the same items for an additional 1¢.

It was the sale of sales.

It was like giving yourself a present.

How in the world could Rexall afford to sell something for 1¢ that regularly cost 89¢?

Folks never did figure that out.

Did they hike up the prices of the original items? No. Did they ship in second-rate merchandise, "sale stuff", somebody asked? No.

No question but that Rexall added to the store's merchandise from its voluminous list of items in its warehouse. But it was still regular merchandise.

Folks were in a festive mood during the 1¢ sale. Dad went to the drug store first with the family, then hiked off to the hardware store to look at tools he might buy, or get some supplies. Mom toured the ladies department in the mercantile to see the new things being offered in ready-to-wear. The kids found friends in town and gathered with them to talk and consume ice cream cones. It was traditional to give the kids a treat during the 1¢ sale.

The heady atmosphere of the sale lingered for a week after it was over. Folks just loved to talk about what they got for a penny.

It was the nearest thing to something for nothing.

What a nice event to enjoy while reaping the benefits.

And to look forward to next year.

The Suit Club

The Depression spawned many an innovative idea. Some were good, some were bad. Some worked, some didn't.

One that worked was the Suit Club. Towns with a clothing store promoted the idea. It stirred up interest in clothing and accessories and it was profitable to the proprietor. People who acquired a new suit were wont to buy a new shirt, a new tie, a pair of socks, and maybe, a pair of shoes. Made the cash register ring. For the customers it was a chance to get a suit of clothes for a dollar or just a few dollars. And, at worst, they got a new suit at the standard price on the installment plan.

Here's how it worked. The proprietor of the clothing store promoted the idea throughout the countryside and signed up 50 men who agreed to pay $1 a week for 25 weeks.

Each week there was a drawing.

The first lucky winner's name was drawn out of a pot and he got his suit for $1. The first $1 he had invested. And so it went: the second week someone got a suit for $2, the third week for $3 and so on. The drawing ended after the 24th week. From then on suits cost $25 each, but there was only one more week to pay and the suit was yours.

The store proprietor made more than 20 percent on his investment, new suits sprinkled the area, a lot of people looked a lot sharper in Church on Sunday, and there was the joy of gambling fever that brought you into the gambit in the first place.

The Suit Club only worked every few years. There was just so much market and you had to wait for new customers to come into the stream before a Suit Club could again be launched.

There was no need for advertising. Those who won these suits in the drawing for $1, or $5 or $10 or any figure in between, never stopped talking about their "good deal."

Everyone was happy in the long run. You paid your money, you took your chances on getting a new suit of clothes for a few dollars, and in the end, if you weren't one of the winners, you had a fine quality, name brand suit at a fair price— and on the easy installment plan.

It was a Depression idea that paid off for everyone.

$1 a Day
and "Keep"

It doesn't seem possible now, but there was a time when $1 a day and "keep" was a satisfactory wage.

The bottom of the Depression saw many workers on farms, on construction jobs, on the railroad, and in many other work places including institutions, laboring for as little was one dollar for at least eight hours of work.

It was enough to buy a few necessities: overalls, work shirts and work gloves, a pair of work shoes once a year, a straw hat for summer and a wool cap with ear flaps for winter, a sheepskin coat that would last for years, over-shoes, tobacco, eyeglasses ordered from an ad in the American Legion magazine, and an occasional glass of beer.

The "keep"—three square meals a day and a clean, warm place to sleep—was equally, even more important. A man could get along just fine if he was well fed and had a good bed seven days a week.

Many a hired man on the farm lived contentedly this way.

There was no greener grass on the other side of the fence. Just be glad you had what you had.

Those who were discontented could join the army or the navy. The pay was almost exactly the same for a private or a seaman, around $1 a day. Food and quarters were standard service style, but there was compensation— lots of security. Didn't have to worry about tomorrow, next week or next year. Uncle Sam took care of everything.

The CCC Camps came along and they were the same: a dollar a day, mess hall food, barracks life, and plenty of hard work. The camps kept tens of thousands of American youths off the streets and provided liberal doses of discipline since the camps were run by military officers.

For all of those who worked for $1 a day and "keep", work days weren't always the modern eight hours in length. More often than not, it was ten hours, especially on the farm.

That worked out to ten cents an hour. A man's "keep" would generously be figured at about $2 a day so, in reality, the worker's income was worth at least $3 a day.

Not bad during the years of the Depression when jobs were scarce and a steady job was a prize to be had.

The majority of the men who worked for $1 a day and "keep" were single. Hired men on the farm traditionally tended to be men who didn't marry. Itinerant workers took a long time, if ever, to settle down with a wife and a permanent address. Young men in their teens or early twenties weren't anxious to get married unless there was room for another family on the family farm or in the family business.

Not for a long time. With the uncertainty of the times, hard times, marriage was something to think about when times got better.

These were the years of a labor intensive society (a term not known then). Work for the most part was done by hand. Farm work was long days of often back-breaking labor with horse-drawn equipment and hand tools. Pick and shovel, saw and hammer, were the tools of the building and construction workers; there were no electric saws and power drills or machine diggers.

Families had it the toughest. Everyone had to work to keep the family fed, clothed and sheltered. One could hardly afford to get sick. Often there was no money for medicines and doctors. Home remedies had to do unless things got so bad the doctor had to be called in as a last resort.

Somehow, folks in small towns and on the farms got through these times— scarred but whole, tired but satisfied, they'd made it through the tough years.

Anyone who ever worked for $1 a day and "keep" was an optimist.

He had to be. Things couldn't get worse.

They could only get better.

Write When You Get Work

During the 1930s an expression often repeated was "Write when you get work."

It was a sign of the times. Hard times.

There was a sad note to it because it meant separation. Husband, father, son, brother would be "heading down the road" looking for work wherever he could find it and wouldn't stop until he did find it.

That could be in the next town, the next county, the next state or another part of the country.

Jobs were scarce during the Great Depression and the 30s were the toughest years.

There also was a note of anticipation in those "goodbye for now" words. Anticipation of a job, money coming in, food and clothing and shelter for the family.

Hope. The hope that things would work out, that everything would be okay, that troubles would be over. The hope that the family would soon be together again.

A prayer went with it. A silent prayer as a loved one went out the gate, down the road, out of sight.

Small towns were hit hard. There was no diversified industry. When things went bad, as they did in the Depression, jobs dried up to the extent there was nothing left to do but leave.

Look for a job somewhere else.

It was worse where the three-year drouth during the 30s devastated much of the Southwest, the West and the Midwest. No crops, plus banks failing and businesses failing was more than any little town could stand.

It's a wonder they survived.

Some of the people didn't recover from the economic chaos. Down to nothing, they simply had to put their lives back together the best they could and go on.

For many of them it was "Write when you get work."

Men would head out, on foot, hitchhiking, riding freight trains— any way to get someplace where they had heard there was a possibility of work. Any kind of work would do.

Back home the folks would wait for word, looking eagerly for a letter or a penny postcard that would tell them the news. Good news, they hoped.

And many times that news did come:

"I've found work. It isn't much, but it's steady and we can live on it. Just as soon as I get paid I'll send for you. Pack just the things we can't do without and bring them. Sell everything else. It'll be a long time before we see the old town again. You can write me General Delivery. Take good care of the kids. Tell them I love them as I love you. Our prayers are answered."

There wasn't always a happy ending, but it did happen. Now there are just faint memories.

But today, when folks of a certain age get together, folks from that era, they still may say as an expression and in the spirit of those old times as they depart from visits or reunions:

"Write when you get work."

A Dollar
For Passing On

The Great Depression produced many unusual changes in the American lifestyle of a small town.

None greater or more needed than the volunteer burial societies. Most folks didn't have life insurance, or if they did, it lapsed for non-payment.

There was just no money for life insurance.

Money was for food, fuel, absolutely necessary clothing.

The money people had in a savings account to lay them away on their passing was lost when the banks failed, and most small town banks failed.

In those days there was no Federal Deposit Insurance Corporation to protect the savings of depositors. The bank closed and that was it.

Your money was gone.

You had to look to something else. Laying a loved one away could be a problem if there was no money for a deserved and proper burial.

Something had to be done about the situation.

Burial societies were formed.

They were usually headed by thoughtful civic leaders.

Concerned for their fellow man, neighbors, acquaintances, the good folks in nearby communities, they organized the societies. They worked.

You pledged that if a member of the society passed on (no one ever said died) you would send one dollar to the family of the deceased.

Pretty good-sized memberships were needed so there would be enough money for the final rites. It was common to have as many as 1,000 members stretched across several counties.

A member passed away. The dollar bills rolled in. Enough for a fine casket supplied by the furniture store (caskets were a type of "furniture") whose proprietor was the local undertaker. It was traditional.

People paid. They had pledged. Sometimes it was the last dollar in their pocket for awhile.

You never knew. It could be your turn next and "a fine laying away" was something the family could be proud of.

The societies lost a few members as time went on, but more often than not the children kept up the memberships. They could be transferred within the family.

Thirty years after one of these was started, it produced 938 one-dollar bills on the death of a member.

The idea was still as strong as ever. It was the right thing to do for the right reason back in those Depression days. And it lasted.

It was worthwhile.

It was people banding together to take care of each other. It was a phenomenon of a small town in the Depression.

Egg Money

Egg money made the difference in the 1920s and 30s. Mostly it was the tender of farmers' wives and town women who had room for a pen and a chicken house, usually at the edge of town.

The women took care of the chickens. They set the eggs under the old hens, they were there at the hatching to make sure the baby chicks were warm and well taken care of, they fed the chickens, cleaned the pens, collected the eggs, washed the eggs, and packed them, usually in a 12-dozen case, ready to go to town and sell.

Eggs were one form of ready cash. The other was cream. Every farm had a few cows and many farmers kept half a dozen or so. In town, or on the edge of town it was usually one, two or three cows— maybe four if you had the room. Since one cow provided enough milk and butter, if you were still churning your own, there was always cream to sell.

But the cream money belonged to the farm or the

family. Dad was in charge of this money. It went for staples: groceries, work clothes, medicine, gas for the car.

Not so the egg money. That was mom's.

She earned it. Plus that, she served up tasty fried chicken throughout much of the year. Then there was chicken and dumplings, chicken soup, and chicken hot dishes. Young fryers were for the skillet; the old hens made the stews and soups and hot dishes.

The well-fed male head of the household let well enough be just that.

The egg money was mom's. She could do what she wanted to with it; of course not to spend foolishly.

Anywhere from 25 to 100 laying hens could produce a lot of eggs.

The old hens worked seven days a week. No rest for them on Sundays.

The kids helped mom collect the eggs, helped her wash the eggs and put them in the egg cases.

Kids are smart. They didn't need to say anything. They knew if they were good helpers there was something in it for them: a sack of candy on Saturday, money for an ice cream cone on band nights, birthday and Christmas gifts.

The eggs went to town once a week— with mom. She collected the money and then began her weekly "special shopping" for those items the cream money didn't pay for. She always had a list. The list never ran out. The money did, but there were always more eggs and more money.

There was variety in the list: spools of thread, pins and needles, yard goods for that special blouse she wanted to make, stamps, envelopes, tissue paper for wrapping gifts, birthday and Christmas gifts, school supplies, once in a great while a shawl or a scarf, delicate underthings which were never mentioned, feathers and ribbon to make a hat, shoe polish, surprise items like a dozen packages of assorted flavors of Kool-Aid with which to surprise the family on hot summer days, that sack of candy the kids expected at shopping time, and money for the ice cream cone treats on band night and for the collection plate at Sunday school and church.

A town merchant once said that more money changed hands because of eggs and cream than anything else. He may have been right. No question but that it kept the cash registers in town ringing.

Saturdays, of course, were the big days, but as time went on and store owners caught on to the profits to be made by keeping the stores open during Wednesday night band concerts, more eggs and cream came to market during the middle of the week.

Egg money had a lot of benefits.

But perhaps most important was it gave mom some independence. She was in charge of the chickens and she was in charge of the egg money. With such a measure of independence went pride. The pride that comes with knowing you are always contributing to the welfare and happiness of the people you loved.

How could you beat that?

The Year
They Paved
Main Street

The year they paved Main Street the town was changed forever. The change was inevitable. Every town, no matter how big, had its ambitions.

All of them believed they would grow, that they had a destiny. The fact that no one had any idea of what that destiny was made no difference. You believed in a bright future, and that was it. In a time long before paved Main Streets, it was the coming of the railroad that would bring the miracle of great growth and a great future. The village would become a booming city—maybe just a booming small city, but a city nevertheless.

It only happened to a few communities scattered around the country that accidentally found themselves in the path of untapped natural resources, a mushrooming industry riding the tides of popular use, or some other dramatic factor. Mostly, though, the towns kept right on being the same. The railroad did bring some new vigor, some new trade, and it was good for the town. But the change was minimal.

Main Street was still Main Street. It was graveled every two years and graded every week. On hot, dusty summer days, the sprinkler wagon, first drawn by horses and later a truck-mounted affair, wet the place down in the cool hours of early morning. By mid-afternoon the street was back to dust. Most folks did their shopping early anyway, or had the store deliver the groceries. So the dust wasn't much of a bother.

Cars proceeded slowly up and down Main Street. You didn't speed on gravel. It just wasn't done, wasn't proper. Tires could throw rocks up on the sidewalks, maybe strike a plate glass window of a store if you got up too much speed. Gravel was the best traffic controller man has ever had.

A gravel Main Street was accommodating. You could spit in it, including tobacco juice. This was okay. Dogs used it for their needs and no one seemed to mind much. The grader would be by in a day or two and clean up everything, make it look smooth and neat again. Horses and ponies, when there were still a lot of them around in the 1920s and early 30s, were another thing. Then the town street cleaner had to make a pass down Main Street every afternoon. Sanitation code you know.

A gravel Main Street didn't stop having an annual festival street dance. A half-dozen town carpenters, public spirited for a day, came together to build a dance floor on the gravel. The day after the big dance, the carpenters would return to take the floor apart and the boards would be hauled back to the lumber yard for sale at a discount, the lumber yard owners calling the difference between the discount price and their normal, hefty profit their annual contribution to the city's promotion.

Folks never had to worry about crossing Main Street safely.

People driving cars weren't in a hurry and if you drove slowly you were noticed more. They waved a friendly hello to friends and neighbors on foot or in their front yards.

150

There were no traffic lights, no stop signs. They would have been considered silly, or "showing off," or perhaps a little preposterous in a town of a few hundred people. Parents didn't have to worry much about their kids crossing Main Street. They just told them to cross at the corners, look each way before crossing, be careful, especially of high-stepping horses pulling a light wagon or buggy. These horses were apt to shy and you never knew what would scare them into a bolt.

Traffic was light. Town residents didn't drive their Model T's or Model A's, Chevies, Dodges or Hudsons just to go downtown. Walking would do that. Farmers drove in only once or twice a week for supplies and that might be by truck or horse and wagon. Cars were used for trips, to park at the band concert so you would have a front-row seat, and on Sundays after church to drive to one of those delicious farm dinners of fried chicken and fresh garden items from the garden at farmer friends in the country. Winters were practically an automobile shutdown. Stay home was the best thing to do— or take the train.

Change came. Here and there another town in the county paved its Main Street and that caused agitation in the old home town. "When are we going to get a paved Main Street? We've got to keep up with the times." Such was the hue and cry for progress, for modernism. The Town Council began to hear from quite a few residents, those anxious to keep up with "the other towns."

There was no stopping it. Main Street had to be paved. It would be a good thing for the town. No more dust. A cleaner Main Street. A better looking business street. Marked parking spaces. Progress.

Oh, it was going to be wonderful. Exciting just to think about it, folks said.

The Town Council stretched its budget, let the bids, signed a contract with a road paving outfit. The Chronicle came out every Thursday with another story about the paving project and the benefits a paved Main Street would bring the town.

Forgotten in the enthusiasm was the quaint, even old-fashioned but always pleasant look the town had with its graveled Main Street. Kind of sedate. Part of the look came from the fact that most stores hadn't changed during the years. In fact, you couldn't tell the difference between 1935, 1925, and even 1915 in some cases.

It was a comfortable look, a comfortable feeling. Town folk were used to it, relaxed about it, accustomed to the way it was, had been for so many years.

It would end now. The paving was coming. Still, most thought it was a good idea and they were promised a new look and a better town.

So Main Street changed, and the town changed, and it was never the same again. Progress. There were those who still had doubts even after it was paved. They weren't so sure it was a good idea. And it cost a lot of money. They were in the minority. Pride in the "new" paved Main Street took over.

Main Street now became something different. It became the fast lane for automobiles finding it convenient to use the slick roadway to get from South of town to North of town or to connect with the East-West highway. They sped through without stopping. Eyes straight ahead. Honked if you even looked like you were getting in the way. Didn't wave at anybody. Some of the young "hot foots" from around the countryside were a special problem. They "goosed" their cars plenty to put on a little show to impress friends and anyone who might be looking, speeding into the center of town and jerking to a stop on Main Street after doing a tight U-turn at the bottom of the street.

Moms and dads now had to run a campaign to get the little kids to be more careful about crossing Main Street.

The danger level had risen. The Town Council talked about that. There were warnings spoken in classrooms at the school.

Horses, still being used, but by fewer and fewer farmers, now kept to the side streets. They were still graveled and would be for decades to come. Horses weren't wanted on Main Street anymore, might mess things up. They didn't represent the new, modern look.

Thus, a picturesque aspect of Main Street was lost. Dogs didn't like it, either. They were shooed away from Main Street. A few of them made the mistake of messing up Main Street and were run off by broom-wielding shopkeepers.

The marshal had to keep later hours to keep the peace. The new, paved Main Street now became an ideal gathering place for cars and kids. On summer nights they piled into their cars and headed for Main Street and a round of cokes. It was a ritual, which sometimes got a little noisy, particularly if there was an invasion by cars and young folks from neighboring towns "come to look things over." "Check things out."

Not all change was easy. The town soon found out it had to spend more money. The old grader wasn't good enough for a paved Main Street and it was shunted off to side street duty. The council had to borrow against the next year's budget to buy a new machine that could clean the snow from the hard top in the winter and had a big roller brush attachment to clean the pavement in the summer when gravel from adjacent streets was carried in by the car tires. A paved Main Street wasn't all it was cracked up to be.

But the biggest change was in the town itself. It was a different town now. It had a new look and it just wasn't the same old town. Paving Main Street led to more hurrying, more speed and changing store fronts to "keep up with the times."

You can't turn the clock back, though. There were folks who would like to have done just that when the news came that they were going to put a stop sign midway on Main Street to slow down traffic.

Who would have thought something like that would ever happen?

Times Sure Have Changed

Life was not complicated in those days when the shadows of World War I still hung over the country and the roots of World War II were just forming in Europe.

While life was uncluttered it wasn't simpler, either. But values stood like solid rock and where there were problems they were faced head-on and worked out. Resolved. Ended.

It was smooth water mostly. Big waves upset the town. They were to be avoided. Follow tradition. Lead the steady life. Get a job, give an honest day's labor, keep the paycheck coming in. You lived up to your responsibilities, paid your taxes, went to church on Sunday, voted in all elections.

New things came along, but slowly. Things changed faster in the city. In small towns it took a lot longer. Folks weren't in a hurry. There was plenty of time.

You had your bacon and eggs every morning. Fried potatoes and thick gravy and good old pork chops and roast beef were regular fare. Meat and potatoes three times a day. It was the custom. No one had ever heard of cholesterol. So they didn't have to worry about it.

There weren't many heart attacks. If you did an honest day's labor and went to bed tired but satisfied you'd done your part, no need to worry about the old heart. Hard work made for strong hearts, they said.

Also, having good thoughts and believing in the Lord. If people passed away suddenly they were "just struck down, right in the prime of life." That could be anywhere from 30 to 70. The usual reason was "it ran in the family." If it didn't run in your family, no need to worry. Some things were just natural and nobody looked very closely at the causes.

Monday was wash day, Tuesday was ironing day, you baked Thursday and Friday. Saturday was bath day and dress up and go to town day.

The only yuppies around were those old-timers who were always saying "yup" like in "yup, it sure looks like it's gonna rain."

If you were getting older and having trouble reading the weekly Chronicle you ordered a pair of eyeglasses through the mail. That took care of that problem.

Gay meant folks having a gay old time. "We sure had a gay old time at the dance Saturday night." Homosexual was a word in the big dictionary at the town library (not in the ones at school). No one ever looked up the word. If there was someone in town who was gay he stayed in the closet. He wanted to stay in town and coming out of that closet was a sure one-way ticket out of town. True, there was always somebody who was considered a little strange. Odd sort of fellow. Folks usually didn't pay much attention. They did wonder, though, why he took those trips out east every year. He said he was adding to his collection of antique daggers, but he didn't bring many back home.

Divorces were so rare one would be talked about for months on end. They were practically unheard of in some communities. Husbands and wives did separate now and then but the bonds never were broken. Vows were vows. Preachers said hell and damnation awaited those who broke the vows.

Women soothed their nerves and eased the digestive system with the popular mail order tonics and elixirs (62% alcohol) and never missed a meeting of the Women's Temperance League.

Menfolk sipped whiskey for medicinal reasons, to be sociable, or to restore male pep. This was done out of sight of the family. Liquor was never kept in the house. If there was a pint or quart of "corn", Kentucky bourbon or Templeton Rye it was hidden behind the paint cans in the shed or snuggled down in a feed box full of oats.

Coordinated wardrobes were in the future. Farmers wore overalls every working day and wore a dress shirt and new overalls when they went to town on Saturdays. A new pair of overalls was used this way for one year and then became work overalls. A new pair was bought and the process repeated.

Women wore cotton prints by day and saved one silk dress for Sundays and another for weddings, confirmations, baptisms and funerals.

You put on your long underwear— men, women and children— with the first heavy frost and you didn't put them away until the first day of summer.

Chaperoning was still a custom. A young man came to call, a parent or aunt sat with the young folks. After the daughter was "spoken for" the rules were relaxed a little. This all changed when America became a mobile society and more than half the families had a car. You courted by taking your intended for a nice ride in the new car. This led to Lover's Lanes where the flames of romance soared in quick time because you had to get back with the car before it was noticed you had been gone a little too long.

There was only one kind of Coca Cola and it never changed. A southern doctor concocted a new brew for the soda fountains and it became popular. It was called Dr. Pepper. Ice cream came in three flavors: vanilla, chocolate and strawberry. Who needed more than that? Horehound candy and licorice were staples. You made fudge and divinity at home and nothing ever tasted so good. Popcorn balls were great at birthday parties and young folks' gatherings.

Going for a Coke, the picture show once a week, or just going for a walk constituted a date. Sometimes you walked up to the school yard, sat in the swings and talked.

In the summer the kids divided in two gangs and played "chalk the walk".

What you couldn't buy in town you ordered out of the catalogue. Or you made it yourself on your sewing machine or at the workbench in the garage. Clothes and shoes were passed down from older kids to younger. Nothing was ever thrown away. When it was too worn to wear it went into quilting, was used for patching, or rags for house cleaning.

Everybody had a garden and everybody canned. The canning season was a busy one. You "put down" dozens of jars of foodstuffs to be consumed during the long winter months until the garden produced again the next summer. A good all-around meal was a balanced diet. And no one dieted that anybody knew about. If you were big, you were big. If you were skinny, you were skinny. What they said was that it ran in the family.

People didn't have to have an exercise routine. There

was enough work to do around the house, in the yard or on the job. That was plenty of exercise. The only jogging anyone knew about was when the coach got mad at the football team and made them take three extra "jogs" around the football field because of a sloppy practice.

Women and girls wore long hair. It was stylish. Men and boys had their hair cut short. If it got below your ear tops it was time for cutting. The only long hair anybody ever saw on men was in pictures from Africa in the *National Geographic*. That was okay. That was their custom. You had to respect customs.

Children were never born out of wedlock. Sure, some young couples had their first born five or six months after the ceremony, but folks just said "sometimes the first born take a lot less time, ya know."

Times sure have changed.

Research and writing completed December 12, 1989